LIGHT and SIGHT

CHARLES GRAMET

LIGHT and SIGHT

Illustrated by LESLIE HAYWOOD

and with photographs

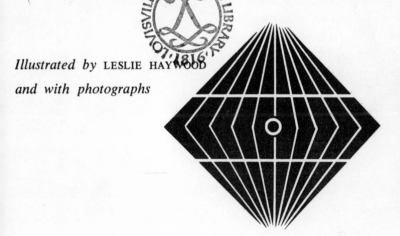

ABELARD-SCHUMAN
London New York Toronto

LONDON
Abelard-Schuman
Limited
8 King Street WC 2

NEW YORK
Abelard-Schuman
Limited
6 West 57th Street

TORONTO
Abelard-Schuman
Canada Limited
896 Queen Street W.

Printed in the United States of America

CONTENTS

List of Illustrations 7

Introduction: Sensing the Environment 9

1 Light and Plant Life 11

2 Light Receptors 21

3 Seeing 33

4 Problems of Seeing 47

5 Seeing Radiant Energy—Color 63

6 Direction of Light 75

7 Seeing the Unseen—The Microscope 91

8 Seeing Through Things—X-Rays 109

9 Seeing Moving Pictures 118

10 Seeing Across Space—Television 124

11 Seeing Farther into Space—Telescope;
   Radar Astronomy 141

12 Laser Light of the Future 154

Index 157

ACKNOWLEDGMENTS

The author gratefully acknowledges generous permission to reproduce the following photographs:

General Biological Supply House, pp. 17, 24, 26, 92 (left), and 103 (a).

The American Museum of Natural History, pp. 28 and 92 (right).

The Pittsburgh Plate Glass Company, p. 51.

Eastman Kodak Company for permission to use photograph from the book *Infrared and Ultraviolet Photography* which appears on page 73, and for photos on pp. 112, 114, 118, 122, and 123.

The United States Army Information Office for U.S. Army Photos on 82 and 137 (top).

Bausch and Lomb Optical Company, pp. 90, 94, 96 (top), and 103 (c), (d), and (e).

American Optical Company, p. 96 (bottom).

The New York Scientific Supply Company, p. 103 (b) and (f).

The United States Navy Information Office for U.S. Navy Photo on 107.

American Telephone and Telegraph, pp. 136 and 137 (bottom).

Mount Wilson-Palomar Observatories, pp. 147, 148, and 150.

Radio Corporation of America, pp. 106 and 125.

ILLUSTRATIONS

Photosynthesis in corn plant 12
Green plant cell—chloroplast 14
One-celled diatoms 17
Food and energy cycles 19
Phototropism 22
Euglena 23
Planaria and structure of eye 24
Nereis and structure of eye 26
Insect head (fly) 28
Structure of compound eye 29
Octopus and structure of eye 30
Structure of human eye 32
Rods and cones of retina 37
Newspaper photograph 40
Enlarged section of photograph 41
Test for blind spot on retina 42
Stereoscopic vision 44
Eye defects and their correction 49
Wheel for testing astigmatism 50
Mirror curvature 51
Disappearing coin trick 53
Refraction of sunlight by earth's atmosphere 54
Optical illusions 55-61
Electromagnetic spectrum 64
Diffraction of light in triangular glass prism 66

List of Illustrations (continued)

Color wheels 67
Photographs on normal film and through red filter 73
Spherical wave front of light wave 76
Incident angle; angle of reflection 79
Mirror periscope 80
The concave reflector 82
Refraction of light 84
Light direction at various angles 86
Light reflected by a prism binocular 87
Convex and concave lenses 88
Plastic cable 90
Stagnant water as seen through microscope 92
Anton van Leeuwenhoek 94
Compound microscope 95
Modern microscopes 96
Focal length of convex lens 98
Images formed by convex lenses 99
Objects seen through microscope 103
The electron microscope 106
Bacteria magnified under optical and electron microscopes 107
X-ray tube 110
X-ray picture of hand and wrist 112
X-ray picture of entire body 114
Film strips 118
Ultra-slow motion picture 122-123
An image-orthican tube 125
A color television broadcast 132-133
Telstar I 136
Dish-shaped antenna and horn-shaped antenna 137
Telescopes 145
The Hale reflecting telescope 147, 148, 150

SENSING THE ENVIRONMENT

Computers, often called "electronic brains," are among the marvels of the electronic age. They can, indeed, solve difficult problems in mathematics and engineering, for example, usually in a small fraction of the time that it would take a human brain to do so. But computers cannot by themselves get information from and about the environment; they cannot perceive or sense, as your brains can do through their sense organs.

Our sense organs enable us to know what goes on about us. We can taste, smell, feel, hear, see. We can then act in response to these stimuli, according to the needs of the moment.

Mostly we learn what goes on about us through our eyes. Through them we know brightness, color, movement. Through our eyes we know the appearance of places, things, people. Our eyes form images.

Science has made it possible for us to extend our sight. We are able to see unseen little things; we can see through things; we can see across space; we can see farther into space. We can see so much more than meets the eye.

1

LIGHT AND PLANT LIFE

Light is radiant energy. All living things are sensitive to it. All living things react to it. All living things are dependent on it.

This is a book about sight. You may think that all animals see. You will learn in this book that ever so many cannot do so. Yet even these are almost always sensitive to light and react to it.

Most animals, however small or simple in structure, have some special part or area that is especially sensitive to light, that is especially adapted to its reception. This does not mean that these animals see. Seeing requires a well-organized organ and a brain.

You may be quite certain that plants do not see. No matter how large or complex in structure a plant is, it has no special part or structure for the reception of light. But plants are sensitive and react to light without the benefit of any special structure for receiving it.

PHOTOSYNTHESIS IN A CORN PLANT

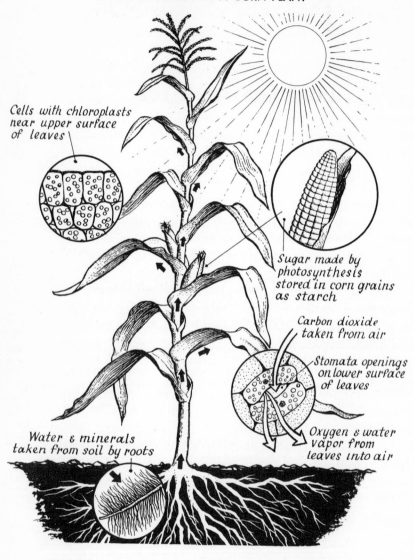

Cells with chloroplasts near upper surface of leaves

Sugar made by photosynthesis stored in corn grains as starch

Carbon dioxide taken from air

Stomata openings on lower surface of leaves

Oxygen & water vapor from leaves into air

Water & minerals taken from soil by roots

Upon this sensitivity, reaction, and use of light all life on Earth depends. Before learning about seeing, let us learn how plants get the benefit of light without sight.

Light enables green plants to make complex chemical compounds from simpler ones that contain atoms of carbon, hydrogen, and oxygen. Some of these complex compounds are foods, such as sugar, which is a fuel. This means that it stores energy, which must have come from sunlight because the plants cannot make sugar without it. This may account for the popular saying that sugar, and other fuel foods, are "canned" sunlight.

This process of making complex chemical compounds out of simpler ones is called photosynthesis. Light supplies the energy. Chloroplasts, the green bodies found in the cells of green leaves, have an important role in converting and storing the energy of the sun.

"Chloroplasts" means "green bodies." They are green because they contain a green pigment called chlorophyll. This is a complex chemical compound that produces other chemical compounds called enzymes. The enzymes can reorganize the atoms of carbon, oxygen, and hydrogen in carbon dioxide and water to make sugar.

Chloroplasts are normally found in leaves, sometimes in the stems of plants. They are rarely found in animals. The one-celled Euglena is one of these exceptional animals that has chloroplasts within it so that it can carry on photosynthesis. This means that it can make its own food, while other animals are dependent on plants for theirs.

Plants can change sugar into starch, or vice versa; and they can change either into fats. Moreover, by adding com-

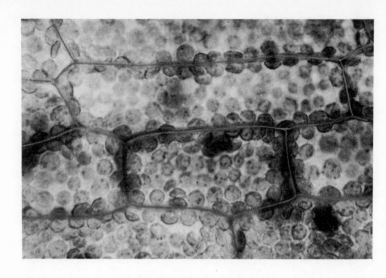

Green plant cell—chloroplast

pounds of nitrogen and other elements from the minerals they take in from the soil, plants can make proteins and vitamins. Despite their apparently simple structure, green plants are remarkable chemical factories.

When you use sugar in your body you release the energy that binds the elements which make up the compound. Carbon dioxide and water are reformed. The released energy, originally light energy, enables you to work and play.

You get some idea of the amount of light energy converted by plants when you know that the corn crop alone in this country yields more than 50 million tons — 100 billion pounds (100 thousand million pounds) — of starch in one year.

Green leaves show their need for light by their response

to it. The leaves of plants growing on a window sill turn their broad blades so that they expose a maximum of surface to the light. If these plants are turned around so that the leaves face away from the sun, the situation will be changed in a few days. The leaves will turn again so that the broad blades are exposed to the sun.

This response of green leaves to light is an example of phototropism, a response that living things make to light.

Green leaves are attracted to the light. Their response is, therefore, positive. Some animals similarly respond to light. They may be attracted to or repelled by it.

In dense jungles leaves react to light by "reaching" for it. The growth of plants is so dense that the trunks of trees grow tall, the stems of vines climb high. Thus the leaves are brought up to the light. They make a green canopy in which a multitude of insects, birds — even mammals — live. In the twilight zone below, the vegetation is scanty, and the animal life is similarly sparse.

Plants have no sense organs. How then are the leaves "aware" of light? The protoplasm, the living material of the leaf stem, is sensitive to it. The response movements result from an increase in growth on the shaded side of the leaf stem, so that it becomes bent in the direction of the light.

Not all plants are so sensitive to light as to respond positively to it. Violets have been called "modest" because they are found growing in shaded places. Many mosses, many ferns, many evergreen trees, sugar maples, beeches, and coffee trees are common plants that grow best in subdued light.

But whether they "prefer" (the scientist says, "are adapted to") bright or subdued light, all green plants are dependent on light for their food. All other life, non-green plants and animals (with some few rare exceptions) depend on the green plants' dependence on light.

The abundant growth of green plants in fields and forests, on farms and in orchards, is more than matched by the luxuriant plant life of the sea. So dense are the gulf weeds, for example, in the Sargasso Sea, that many stories have been written of ships that, having become enmeshed, could not escape from them and were lost. The stories are fiction, but the density of the weeds is real. This region is an area in the North Atlantic extending over 800 thousand square miles.

However, most of the plant growth of the seas is invisible. It is made up mostly of microscopic plants, known as diatoms and dinoflagellates. The many kinds are beautifully and intricately formed. Sometimes large patches of the sea become colored by the growth of some of these plants; and, at night, ships will sail through a sea aglow with their phosphorescence.

All over the seas that make up two-thirds of the surface of the Earth, there is a layer of water, never more than 50 yards deep, that teems with microscopic green plant life, forming the bulk of what is called the plant plankton — the floating plants of the sea.

Plant plankton makes possible the abundant life of the seas. These microscopic plants are at the bottom of a food chain that feeds the enormous number and variety of fish and other sea creatures, from the tiny shrimp to the giant whale. It has been estimated that the yield of vegetable

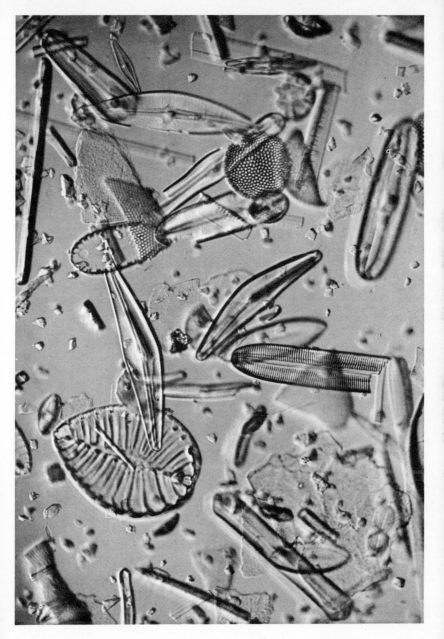

One-celled diatoms seen through a microscope

matter of the oceans is about 10 tons to an acre each sea-
son. Farming the seas may some day supply the food for
Earth's rapidly expanding human population.

The green plants of the sea, like those of the land, must
have light to live, to make food from simple materials. But
light does not penetrate very far into the sea; it is gradually
absorbed as it passes through water.

The red rays in sunlight are necessary for photosynthesis. Yet these rays are the most readily absorbed in water.
Even at a depth of 30 meters (a little less than 100 feet) a
diver cannot see red objects as red. There is no red light
for them to reflect, so that they appear black.

Plant plankton is found, therefore, in the surface layer
of the waters of the seas. It is most abundant up to a depth
of 10 meters (about 35 feet). Considerable amounts may
be found to a depth of 50 meters. This distribution varies
somewhat with the time of day and year, and with the
latitude.

Plankton is much more abundant in the waters of the
temperate zone and of the Arctic than in the seas of the
torrid zone. Moreover, near the Earth's poles the plant
plankton is found closer to the surface. This is because the
sun's rays are more slanting in these regions. Slanting rays
of light do not penetrate as deeply as do those that strike
the water in a more direct line.

A great variety of animal life feeds on the plant plankton, and in turn is fed on by carnivorous animals. The main
mass of this sea life is, therefore, close to the surface. This
explains the presence of great flocks of marine birds in the
Arctic. They find an abundant food supply easily available

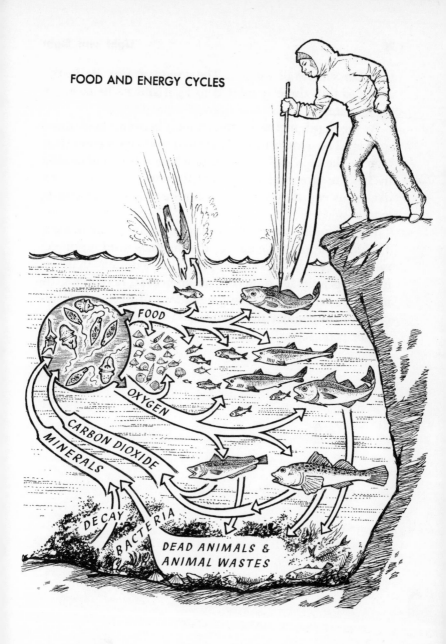

FOOD AND ENERGY CYCLES

near the surface of the sea. The abundance of life in the Arctic is thus directly related to light and its behavior in these waters.

As the depth increases, the animals become smaller and sparser. The food supply is limited and uncertain. It is, largely, the debris of the layer in which it is manufactured by the tiny green plants. While the fish of the deep look like monsters, they are small monsters, a foot or less in length.

Light supplies the energy that green plants store in food. This food supplies the energy that animals need for movement, for work. It also supplies the materials that living things need for growth. And, moreover, it supplies the materials for starting new generations of plants and animals. Small wonder that plants and animals are sensitive and respond to it.

2

LIGHT RECEPTORS

Animals, with few exceptions, move about to seek food, or to avoid being used as food. They do so, also, to seek a more favorable environment, or to escape from an unfavorable one.

Light plays an important role in animal movement. Even the simplest animals — one-celled, microscopic protozoa — are sensitive and react to light.

A drop of water from a stagnant pond, seen under a microscope, shows how such animals behave in response to light. A bright light illuminates one side of the drop.

The tiny, irregularly-shaped bits of living matter called *amebae* move to the less bright side. So, too, do the trumpet-shaped *Stentors*. The common slipper-shaped paramecia appear neutral. They swim in and out of either area.

A closely related slipper-shaped animal that swallows and harbors green, one-celled plants swims to the light side. So do *Euglenae,* one-celled animals that have chloroplasts within them.

The movements of these protozoa are examples of phototropism. The animals that are attracted to light respond positively. Those that shun light respond negatively.

In most protozoa the entire animal is light-sensitive. There are some, however, that have a spot that is especially light-sensitive. Each *Euglena* has such a spot. It is called an eye spot.

The sensitive, light-detecting eye spot of an *Euglena* is useful, indeed necessary, to orient the tiny animal to the best position to obtain the light necessary to make its food. It isn't surprising, therefore, that *Euglenae* are found near the surface of ponds, or of an aquarium.

The eye spot of an *Euglena* is not, however, an eye. Protozoa do not look at or for things. They do not "see." See-

PHOTOTROPISM

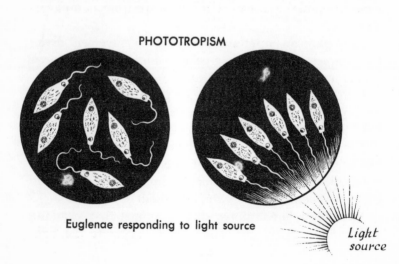

Euglenae responding to light source

Light source

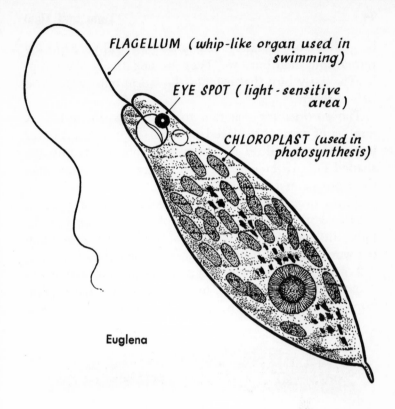

FLAGELLUM *(whip-like organ used in swimming)*

EYE SPOT *(light-sensitive area)*

CHLOROPLAST *(used in photosynthesis)*

Euglena

ing requires that an image be formed and focused. The eye spot of an *Euglena* is a simple light receptor, a part that is especially sensitive to light waves.

Earthworms, likewise, do not see. Yet they are very sensitive to light. Fishermen who use them as bait hunt for them at night, when the worms come out of their burrows in the earth to feed. A flashlight will spot them. They must be grabbed immediately; otherwise they will very quickly retreat into their burrows. They are negatively phototropic. The early bird that catches the worm must also do so before dawn.

The *earthworms'* reaction to light is easily tested. A number of worms are placed on moist soil in a box. A cover is placed over half of it. The worms soon crawl into the shaded side. If the cover is then shifted to the other side, the worms crawl to that side.

Earthworms have light-sensitive cells scattered throughout the skin. No matter what part of the body receives the light, the sensation is carried by nerves to what little brain the worm has, and it withdraws from the light.

A more primitive worm is *planaria,* a small flat worm about half an inch long. It lives under stones and vegetation in ponds and streams, and swims about to seek its food.

Planaria and
the structure of its eye

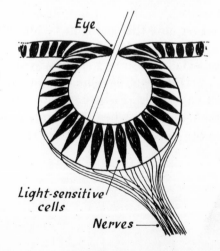

Eye

Light-sensitive
cells

Nerves

Planaria has a clearly formed head. On its upper surface there are two eyes.

The eye of *planaria* is like a small, hollow cup. It is covered with a dark pigment, except at one spot. The inside of the eye is lined with light-sensitive cells. The ends of the cells are drawn out to form nerves which lead to a very simple brain.

This eye cannot form an image. It may be compared to a photo-electric cell. Such an instrument is used to detect light and to measure its intensity. It uses a chemical which is very sensitive to light to change light energy into electrical energy. In this way the intensity of the light is measured. A photographic light meter is a photo-electric cell, for example.

In the *planaria* eye, light enters through the spot that is not covered with pigment. The light-sensitive cells in the eye change light energy into nerve impulses. The nerve impulses are carried to the worm's very simple brain. The reaction of the worm is to move away from the light. This is a negative response. The worm seeks the protection of the dark, under rocks and vegetation.

This reaction of *planaria* is simply and interestingly shown. Several worms are placed in a dish of water in a dark room. When the light from a small flashlight is shone on the worms, from behind them, they move away from the light. When the direction of the light is changed, the worms change their course. They can be steered by changing the direction of the light that is shone on them.

A close relative of the *earthworm* is the worm called *Nereis*, found near the shore of the sea. There are two eyes in its head.

The eye of *Nereis* is a considerable improvement over that of *planaria*. It is a hollow sphere lined with light-sensitive cells. These cells have rod-like ends that point into the hollow sphere. Such a layer of cells may be called a retina.

A clear, jelly-like material in the eye acts as a lens to concentrate the light on the rods. The other ends of the cells are continued as nerve fibers which join to form an optic nerve, which leads to a brain — again a simple one. A transparent layer, the cuticle, covers and protects the eye.

The eye of *Nereis* is also a photo-electric cell, a more sensitive one than that of *planaria*. It may even form some kind of image. But it has no means of focusing it. Many jellyfish and starfish have similar eyes, consisting of a cluster of light-sensitive cells in a hollow ball, covered by a glassy substance that concentrates light on the cells.

Among the animals without backbones, the most num-

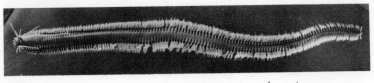

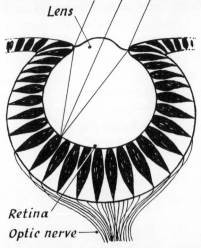

Nereis (sandworm) and the structure of its eye

Lens

Retina

Optic nerve —→

erous, both in kind and number, are the arthropods, the jointed-footed animals. The most numerous arthropods are the insects and the crustacea. The latter include lobsters, crabs, shrimps and similar animals.

Arthropods have very special eyes. They are called compound eyes because each eye is made up of hundreds, sometimes thousands of separate, independent seeing units.

Each unit of a compound eye is made up of several light-sensitive cells, surrounded by pigmented, dark-colored cells. These dark cells screen the unit from neighboring units. At the surface of the unit is a lens that concentrates the light on the light-sensitive cells.

The eye of a bee, of a butterfly, of a lobster, of a crab forms an image. It is a mosaic image. A mosaic picture is one that is made up of many separate pieces. You have seen such pictures on tiled walls or floors. Each unit of a compound eye sees one piece of the whole picture.

A compound eye seems better designed to detect movement than to record the details of an image. The movements would be readily detected on successive units. Some insects do appear to form images, though. Thus a bee, in gathering nectar and pollen from flowers, flies from one flower to another of the same kind. And insects have been seen trying to get nectar from pictures of flowers on wallpaper.

Among the animals without backbones, octopuses, squids, and cuttlefish, all related molluscs, have "camera" eyes. Such eyes form and focus images. This is seeing. Strangely, although these animals are not even remotely related to mammals in structure, their eyes are quite similar to those of mammals.

The large, rounded areas on the sides
of this fly's head are its compound eyes

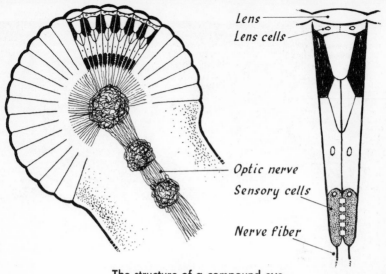

Lens
Lens cells
Optic nerve
Sensory cells
Nerve fiber

The structure of a compound eye

All animals with backbones have camera eyes. But while all cameras work the same way in principle, they may be quite different in operation.

For example, a fish has a different problem in seeing from that of an animal that lives on land, or in the air. The intensity of light, as I mentioned before, falls off rapidly with depth in the water. Besides, the water is always more or less turbid because of the many tiny plants and animals that float or swim about in it, or because of the particles of sand or clay that are carried in it.

Fish, therefore, see near objects more easily than they do far ones. Their eyes are normally set for near sight. They must be focused for far sight. Fish focus for far or near sight by moving the lens of the eye backward or forward, as a camera is focused.

Octopus and the structure of its eye

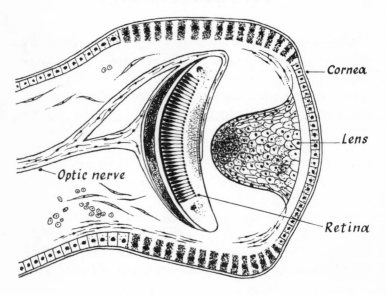

Cornea

Lens

Optic nerve

Retina

Some fish live in the very dimly-lit depths of the sea. They have solved their seeing problem with telescopic eyes. These eyes do not really act as telescopes, which make far objects appear nearer. The name comes from the fact that the eyes extend from the head.

Telescopic eyes sacrifice range or area of vision to the need for collecting the little light in the environment. The eyes are like the central core of a large eye with a spherical lens. The central part of a lens concentrates the light most directly. Fish with telescopic eyes can see only objects that are directly in front of them.

Seeing begins with simple light receptors. They enable the simple animals to make the necessary adjustments to their environment. Eyes that form and focus images enable other animals to adjust to more complex environments. The images that you see are more than camera images. Your mind contributes to them.

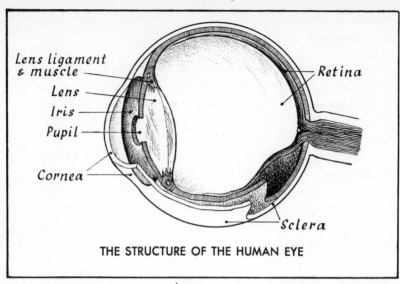

Lens ligament & muscle
Lens
Iris
Pupil
Cornea
Retina
Sclera

THE STRUCTURE OF THE HUMAN EYE

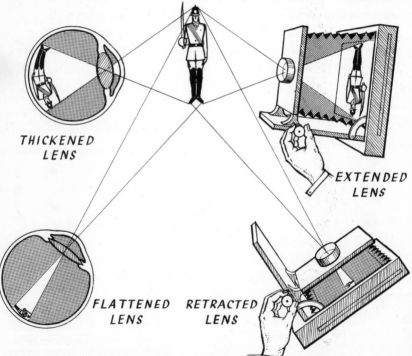

THICKENED LENS

EXTENDED LENS

FLATTENED LENS

RETRACTED LENS

Accommodation by the eye compared with focusing in a camera

3

SEEING

We have camera eyes. This means that our eyes form and focus images, somewhat as a camera does. If, therefore, you know how a camera takes a picture, it will help you to understand how the eye sees. But there were eyes before there were cameras, so that it is really the camera that works somewhat as the eye sees, rather than the other way around. Seeing is far more complex than photography, for the eye is a living structure.

The eyes are spheres, although they may sometimes be somewhat misshapen. Then they do not see clearly. The eyeballs are whitish except for a round, clear, transparent part in front. The white cover of the eyeball is the sclera. It is tough and fibrous, a protective cover. The transparent part, the window of the eye, is the cornea.

Behind the cornea is the circular, colored iris. It may be blue or brown, some shade of each, or a mixture of both. The color of the iris has nothing to do with seeing. But the iris has an important role in vision. The round hole in the iris is the pupil.

Do a simple experiment to see how the iris works. Stand close to a mirror with a bright light on your face, and your eyes wide open. Cover one eye with the palm of a hand so that no light reaches the eye. Hold it there for a minute or so, then pull it away quickly. Be ready to observe the eye that was covered.

In the dark, the pupil of the covered eye will have become larger than that of the uncovered eye. But the enlarged pupil quickly adjusts to the bright light and becomes smaller, to match the other eye. Try this experiment several times, with either eye.

Too little light produces a dim, indistinct image. Too much light produces a glare so that the image is blurred. We cannot see well in either case. The iris controls the situation.

The iris includes many very fine muscle fibers. Some are arranged radially, others are circular. In dim light the radial muscles contract, so that the pupil becomes larger. In bright light the circular muscles contract, so that the pupil becomes smaller.

The tiny muscle fibers act automatically. And the two sets of muscles work in harmony, so that when one set contracts the other relaxes. The iris thus controls the amount of light that enters the eye.

The function of the diaphragm of a camera is like that of the iris of the eye. On most cameras the diaphragm must be set by hand so that the right amount of light reaches the film. Too little light results in an underexposed picture;

too much light in an overexposed one. Neither is a good reproduction of the original.

There are now cameras in which the diaphragm is set automatically, like the iris of the eye, according to the brightness of the light that reaches the camera. With such a camera the picture is almost certain to be well-exposed because the diaphragm admits the right amount of light.

An eye doctor, an ophthalmologist, uses a small, round mirror with a peephole in the center of it to look into the eye through the pupil. He sees that the eye has a lens behind the iris. He sees, also, the thin wall that lines the eye. This is the retina. It is like the film in a camera.

When light from the sun, or from a lamp shines on an object, light rays are reflected from it. Every spot on the object reflects a ray of light. The brightest spots reflect the brightest rays.

The reflected rays of light pass through the transparent cornea. As they do so they are converged. The cornea acts as a lens. When the rays of light reach the lens behind the iris, they are further converged. As a result they are focused sharply on the retina, so that a clear image is formed.

The lens of a camera must be focused to take near or far objects. This is done by moving it forward or backward — forward to focus near objects, backward to focus far objects. The lens in a fish's eye focuses in this way.

See how readily your eyes change their focus for near or far sight. Hold this book in front of you so that you can read it easily and clearly. Can you at the same time see a picture on the wall? You will see it as a blurred image. Still holding the book in the same position, look at the picture on the wall so that you see it clearly. Can you at the same time read the print in the book? Now the letters will be blurred.

The cornea does most of the focusing of the light rays. The lens completes and corrects the focus for near or far sight. The lens changes its shape to do so. It becomes thicker in the center, more convex, for near vision. It becomes flattened, less convex, for far vision. This is called accommodation.

A ligament that is attached to the rim of the lens stretches it so that it is rather less convex. This means that normally, when the eye is at rest, it is focused for far sight. To focus for near objects, tiny muscles oppose the pull of the ligament. This relaxes the tension on the lens so that it becomes more convex. The lens of the eye is flexible, not hard like a glass lens.

As a result of accommodation, the light rays are properly focused on the retina of a normally-shaped eye. The retina is made up of a network of very fine nerve fibers. Each fiber ends in a very tiny rod or a very tiny cone.

Each rod and each cone contains a chemical that is very sensitive to light. The chemical in the cones is called iodopsin, that in the rods is rhodopsin. Both chemicals are pale, reddish pigments.

When the rays of light strike the rods or cones, they bleach the chemical pigments in them. The brighter the ray, the more molecules of the pigment are bleached. This is an example of photochemical change, a chemical change brought about by light. The pigments are changed into a

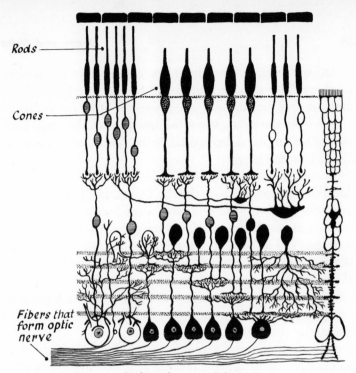

Rods and cones of the retina

chemical called retinene. At the same time some energy is released. This becomes a nerve impulse in a nerve fiber.

Some of the retinene may be changed into Vitamin A. Both the retinene and the Vitamin A may be reconverted in the cones and rods into the light-sensitive pigments — iodopsin and rhodopsin. If the bright light shines on the retina for some time, more pigment is bleached than is reconverted. An excess of Vitamin A is then carried off in the blood stream.

For any brightness of light the eye quickly establishes a balance between bleaching and the reconversion of the retinene and Vitamin A to the photo-sensitive pigments. In bright light the balance is established in two or three minutes. This is called light adaptation. Dark adaptation to dim light takes longer.

Have you ever had an experience like this? You enter a darkened moving-picture theatre from a bright lobby. You "can't see a thing." But in a little while your eyes "get used to the darkness." You can dimly make out the seats and the people in them. You cannot see the people clearly, but you can get by them without stepping on their feet or sitting on their laps as you make your way to a seat.

It is, of course, a matter of becoming dark-adapted. It takes the eyes perhaps half an hour, or more, to become adapted to dim light. It depends on the dimness of the light and the availability of Vitamin A in the blood. The adaptation is made more quickly if there is an adequate supply of the vitamin. In dim light the rods use it for conversion into rhodopsin.

The action of the rods in dim light may be seen in this experiment. Put two circles of white paper, each about an inch wide, on a wall, about a foot apart. Cover one of your eyes with one hand. Look directly at one of the circles with the uncovered eye. You will also see the second circle, but less clearly.

Now have a friend slowly darken the room by drawing the shades or blinds. As the room becomes dark the circle you are looking at disappears, but the other one can still be seen. Next shift your eye so that you look directly at the second circle. Now it disappears, but the first one reappears.

When you look directly at an object, the light rays from that object are focused on cones in the central part of the retina. As the room gets dark, these cones stop seeing. The circle that is focused on them disappears. The second circle is still seen because it is focused on other cones and rods, especially rods. They function as the room becomes dark. When you shift your eye to the second circle you bring it to focus on the central cones, so that it disappears.

This experiment explains why, in the dark, we see more clearly objects that are on the borders of a scene. It explains, also, why we see over a wider area at night, although not clearly. There is a concentration of cones in the center of the retina that enables you to see well in bright light. The rods that enable you to see in dim light are more widely dispersed on the retina.

The eyes of cats have more rods than cones. They therefore see better by night than they do by day. Hence they prowl about by night scavenging for food and hunting mice. Owls sleep by day and fly about by night to hunt for mice and other small animals. Their eyes also have more rods than cones.

On the other hand, hawks have very sharp vision in the daytime because their eyes have so many cones. We are normally more active in the daytime because our eyes have so many cones in the central part of the retina for keen sight in bright light.

Some people see very poorly or not at all in dim light, or at night. They suffer from night blindness. It may be due to a lack of Vitamin A in the blood. This, as you know, is necessary for conversion to rhodopsin in the rods, which are used in seeing in dim light. Good night vision is important to people who drive cars at night, and to pilots who fly planes at night, even though the latter have instruments to guide them.

The nerve impulses that start in the rods and cones move through the many fine nerve fibers of the retina. They all join to make up the large optic nerve. All the separate nerve impulses are carried through it to an area in back of the brain. This is the "seeing center." Here the nerve impulses are interpreted as spots of brightness.

The image that is produced in the brain may be compared with a photograph that is printed in a newspaper. If you look very closely at such a photograph, or examine it with a magnifying glass, you see that it is made up of many very small dots. Some areas appear very dark because they are crowded closer together. Others appear light because they are smaller and are more widely spaced. From the

A newspaper photograph

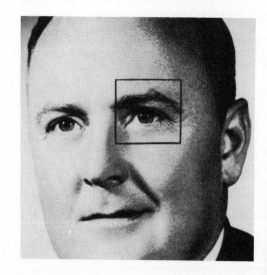

normal seeing distance the dots merge so that you see a smooth picture. The image in the brain is similarly produced by spots of brightness.

People have been blinded by being struck on the back of the head. They lost their sight because the seeing center was damaged, even though the eyes were uninjured. If the optic nerve were damaged, a person could not see because the nerve impulses from the retina could not get through to the seeing center in the brain.

Each of your eyes has six million cones and 160 million rods. Nerve impulses from the rods and cones are carried by nearly a million nerve fibers that make up the optic nerve. The nerve impulses are changed to images in the brain. These images may even be filed in the brain, as you might file snapshots in an album, or movies on a reel of film. That is how you are able to recall the appearance of a person, place, or thing, or of an event. Seeing is not as simple as taking a picture with a camera.

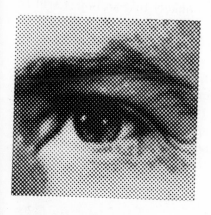

An enlarged section of photograph

There are two spots on the retina that have important roles in seeing. Try this spot test.

Cover your left eye with your left hand. Next hold this book in front of you with your right hand. Keep your right eye fixed on the cross mark. Now move the book s-l-o-w-l-y toward your right eye. At first you see both the circle and the cross. As you bring the book nearer the eye there will be a place, perhaps six inches or less from the eye, when the circle disappears.

The circle is now focused on the retina at the "blind spot." This is the place where the optic nerve meets the retina. From here the fibers of the nerve spread out to every part of the retina. There are no rods or cones at this spot. Hence it is blind.

The blind spot does not usually bother us in seeing. We see with two eyes and it is unlikely that an object will be focused on the blind spots of both eyes at the same time. Besides, we shift our eyes a little all the time so that no part of a scene or of an object remains focused on the blind spot for very long. Moreover, the mind would fill in any blank spots in the image in the brain.

Another spot is seen on the retina as a small, yellow pit. This is the fovea. At this spot there are only cones. They are very tightly packed, about 10,000 of them. Each has a separate nerve fiber from it to the brain.

Cones of the fovea enable us to see most clearly. These cones make it possible, for example, for you to see well such small things as the letters that you are reading here. And it is the fovea that makes it possible for you to enjoy fully all the colors of the rainbow.

Cones are found all over the retina, six million in all. They help us to see in bright light. But the clearest part of any image is that which is focused on the fovea.

Not all animals have cones that can see color. Apes, many birds, a few fish, and some reptiles share color vision with us. For most animals, however, it is a gray world, like a black-and-white photograph of a colored scene.

We can see well with either eye, with the other eye closed. If each eye forms an image of an object, why do we need two eyes? And why do we not see double when we see with both eyes?

Normally we do not see double. Our two eyes are automatically controlled so that the line of sight of each eye is directed toward the same object. An image of the object is focused on corresponding points of the two retinas. Nerves from the corresponding points produce a single image in the brain.

But we can see double. As you look at an object, gently push one eyeball a little. At once you see a double image. The line of sight of this eye is displaced. The light rays from the object are focused on different points of the retinas of the two eyes. The brain interprets this as two images.

Sometimes the muscles that move the eyeballs may not work normally. There are three pairs on each eyeball. They enable you to move your eyes in the many ways that you do. The muscles work in opposing pairs. As a muscle contracts, its opposing muscle relaxes. The amount of relaxation is balanced by the amount of contraction.

When a pair of eye muscles does not work in harmony in this way, the result is "crossed eyes." A child may be born with such eyes, or the condition may develop when the two eyes do not see equally well. In any case, crossed eyes cannot direct their lines of sight at the same place. As a result they see double, unless the condition is corrected.

People who have imbibed too freely of alcoholic drinks may see double. They lose control of their eye muscles so

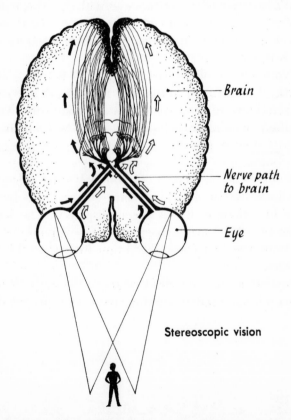

Brain

Nerve path to brain

Eye

Stereoscopic vision

that the lines of sight of their two eyes cannot be directed at the same place.

With two eyes placed as ours are, we see more than we could with one eye. The two eyes cover a larger area. We also see better because with two eyes we have stereoscopic vision.

The image formed by each eye is recorded from a slightly different angle, but on corresponding points on the retina. This gives the impression in the brain of three dimensions. The picture on a canvas or a photographic print has two dimensions — length and width. Stereoscopic vision adds the third dimension, depth. You may have seen this described popularly as "3-D" vision.

Even with one eye we may enjoy stereoscopic vision. We focus the principal part of a scene, or of anything that we look at, on the cones of the fovea. The borders of the field of view are seen less sharply on the other cones (in bright light). This gives the impression of stereoscopic vision.

Moreover, our past experience helps us to see stereoscopically. We "know" that the scene we are looking at has depth, that the object we are looking at is solid, not flat. The mind adds something to the image in the brain.

The image in the brain is right side up, although the image on the retina is upside down, like the image on the film in a camera. The camera image is righted when it is printed. The retinal image is righted in the brain.

Some scientists tried an experiment on themselves. They wore spectacles with lenses that formed images on the retina that were right side up. The experimenters found themselves living in a world that really appeared upside down. At first they found it difficult to move about and work in this strange world. In a few weeks, though, the abnormal world became normal for them. They were able to carry on their usual activities efficiently in their upside-down world.

Then they removed their spectacles, so that the images on their retinas were normal — upside down. Their brains then turned these images right side up. Now the normal world appeared abnormal to the experimenters. They had become accustomed to the upside-down world. They now had to learn to live in the normal world.

A camera records an exact image of an object or of a scene. Seeing is more than that. Other senses may contribute to the retinal image. For example, an infant learns about the size, shape, and texture of an object with its hands and mouth as well as with its eyes. This information becomes a part of its memory of the image of the object.

Past experience may contribute to the retinal image so that the mental image is not identical with it. We may see an object as we remember it, or even as we would have it appear. And because some people do not look attentively, the mental image may be much less exact than the retinal image. If you were to ask a number of people who saw the same incident to describe it, you would undoubtedly get a number of different versions, although the retinal images must have been the same.

Seeing, then, is more than a physical-chemical process. It is a mental process as well. In a way, we learn to see. We may learn to see better.

4

PROBLEMS OF SEEING

An eye does remarkably well in seeing. But it isn't perfect. We may not see well because the eye is defective in structure. Sometimes our eyes fool us.

Have you ever seen someone hold a book or a newspaper so close to his eyes in reading that it almost touches his nose? On the other hand, have you ever seen anyone hold a book or newspaper at arm's length for reading? The first person is nearsighted, the second is farsighted. Both have trouble focusing the print on the retina when the book or newspaper is held at the normal, comfortable distance of 15 inches.

What makes an eye nearsighted? Usually it is that the eyeball is somewhat elongated. Or it may be that the cornea is too spherical for the normally shaped eyeball. In either case the image would be focused in front of the retina and the seen image would be blurred, not clear.

Farsightedness may result from an eyeball that is somewhat shortened. Or it may be that the cornea is not spheri-

cal enough for the normally shaped eyeball. In either case
the image would be focused behind the retina and the seen
image would, again, be blurred, not clear.

The lens of the eye cannot accommodate enough to compensate — make up — for the defect that causes nearsightedness. That is, the lens cannot become thin enough, sufficiently less convex, to focus the image on the retina. In
the farsighted eye the lens cannot accommodate enough,
become sufficiently convex, to compensate for the defect of
the eye so that the image would be focused on the retina.

Spectacles, "eye glasses," are used to assist the lens of the
eye to accommodate in nearsighted or farsighted eyes.
They were invented about four hundred years ago —
around the time that the use of printed books was becoming widespread.

When someone feels there is something wrong with the
way he is seeing, an eye doctor examines the eye to discover in what way it is defective. He then matches a lens for
each eye that will compensate for the lack of accommodation of the eye lens. An optometrist grinds the lenses according to the doctor's prescription. They may be mounted
in a plain frame or in a very ornamental one, or worn without a frame. Contact lenses are very small. They are placed
directly on the cornea.

In the case of the nearsighted eye, the corrective lens
will be concave, one that is thinner in the center than
around the edge. Such a lens diverges, spreads, light rays.
The correction consists in diverging the light rays just
enough before they reach the eye. The cornea and the lens
of the eye will then focus the rays sharply on the retina.

A farsighted eye is corrected with a convex lens. This will

EYE DEFECTS AND THEIR CORRECTION

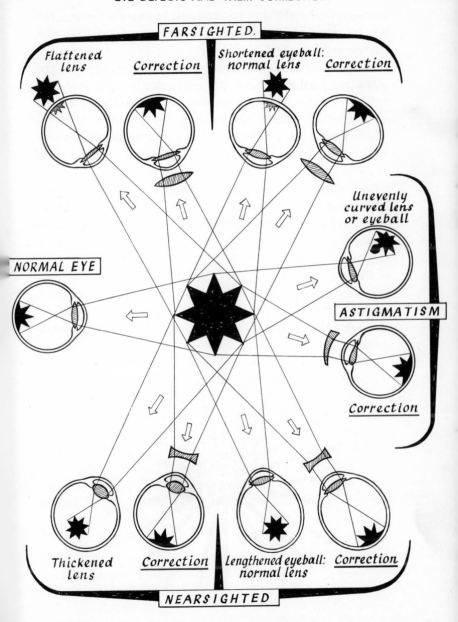

converge the light rays just enough before they reach the
eye so that the cornea and the lens can focus the rays
sharply on the retina.

Only one eye may be defective in structure, while the
other eye is normal. Or both eyes may be defective, but
not to the same degree. Then the corrective lenses will, of
course, be different for the two eyes.

The lens of the eye becomes less elastic as people become
older. As a result it cannot accommodate as well for near
or close vision. When a person begins to hold the printed
page farther and farther from his eyes in reading, it is time
for him to be fitted with corrective lenses. Most persons
over forty-five years of age need glasses to read with comfort.

Many older people wear bifocal lenses. The upper part
of the lens is a correction for normal vision; the lower part
is a correction for close vision, as in reading. Far vision is
not greatly impaired.

Look at the wheel with one eye at a time. Do all the

spokes appear equally clear, equally black? If they do not, the eye may have a defect called astigmatism.

An astigmatic eye has a cornea or a lens whose surface is not perfectly spherical. Either one may be shaped more or less like part of the surface of a cylinder. You may have seen in amusement parks mirrors that have such shapes.

The curvature of the surface
of the mirror affects the image

The images in such mirrors are distorted. A person may appear very tall and extremely thin, or very squat and broad; or the upper part of the body may be shortened while the lower part is lengthened.

A cylindrical cornea or lens produces a vague image because horizontal lines will be focused at one point while vertical lines will be focused at a different point. The correction for astigmatism is a lens of cylindrical form in which the curvature is at right angles to that of the eye defect.

The correction of a defective eye is more difficult if it is both astigmatic and near- or farsighted. Then the correcting lens corrects one of the defects on its front surface, and corrects the other defect on its rear surface.

The type of correction of the lens of a pair of eyeglasses can be easily known. If printed words appear large through the lens (a convex lens) the correction is for farsightedness. If the printed words appear smaller (concave lens) the correction is for nearsightedness. If, as the lens is rotated or twisted, the words are distorted, the correction is for astigmatism.

Even when the eyes see normally, we may not see things as they really are. There is an old saying that "seeing is believing." Let's test it.

Try this disappearing coin trick. It is a very old one that has been known for several thousand years. Place a coin in the bottom of a bowl. Then step back until the coin just disappears from sight. Have a friend slowly pour water into the bowl, without moving the coin. As the water rises in the bowl, the coin comes into view.

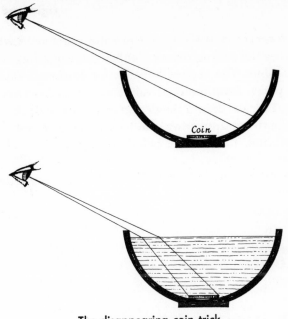

The disappearing coin trick

This is not really a trick at all when you recall that light rays are bent as they pass from water into air (or from air into water). The trick turns out to be an example of refraction.

Have you noticed that a spoon in a glass of water appears to be bent? Have you ever tried to net a fish in an aquarium, only to find that it isn't where it appears to be as you look into the aquarium? Have you ever tried to dip a golf ball out of a water trap? When you reach for it, it isn't where it appears to be. These are errors of sight due to refraction.

Astronomers knew several thousand years ago that they could see the setting sun after it had set, according to their calculations. The rays of light from the sun are refracted as they pass from the relatively empty space between the sun and the earth into the denser atmosphere of the earth. It is like the disappearing coin trick, in reverse. We see the sun set after it has passed below the horizon.

Refraction of sunlight by the Earth's atmosphere

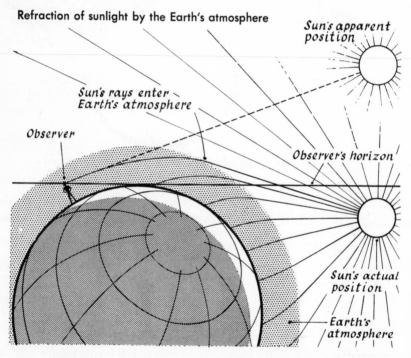

If the eyes are normal in structure, and seeing is not complicated by refraction, may we then believe what we see?

Which line is shorter? Is the hat as wide as it is high?

Measure them. Horizontal lines are easier to see than are vertical ones. This is so because the eyeball moves more easily from side to side than it does up and down. A horizontal line therefore appears to be shorter than a vertical line of the same size.

Which of each pair of lines is shorter? Measure them to

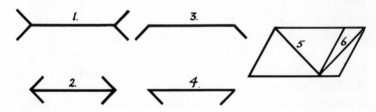

make sure that they are really equal in length. If the eyes are directed inward (lines 2 and 4) the lines appear shorter than if the eyes are directed outward (lines 1 and 3). Does this explain why line 5 appears to be longer than line 6?

Will lines 1 and 2 meet at point 0?

Are lines 3, 4, 5 really parts of the same straight line?

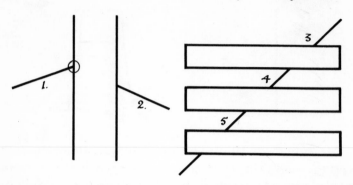

In these cases the eyes are thrown "off the beam," as fliers say. As the eyes travel along the straight line they are deflected — turned aside — when the line cuts across the parallel lines. When the eyes pick up the line again, it appears to be off slightly.

Look at the top diagram on the facing page.

Hold your eyes about 6 inches from the long, straight lines in each of the figures, close to the letter O. Do the lines run parallel? Now hold the book in the normal reading position. The parallel lines appear to bulge in figure A; they appear to bend toward one another in figure B; they appear to go off in different directions in figure C.

The reason is that the lines that cut across the parallel lines disturb your eyes and deflect them, so that the parallel lines do not appear to be so.

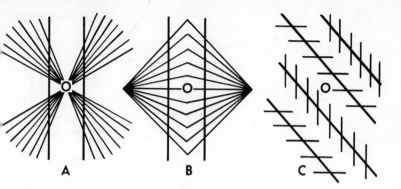

The examples that you have seen so far show you that the movements of your eyes may result in an illusion, a misleading image of the real thing.

Your eyes can fool you about the size of an object. Is circle A smaller than circle B? Measure them.

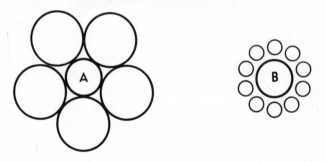

The reason circle A appears smaller is that it is surrounded by larger circles. Circle B appears to be larger because it is surrounded by smaller circles. This illusion is due to contrast. An object may appear different from what it is because it is contrasted with objects around it.

Which of the small discs appears to be the darkest?

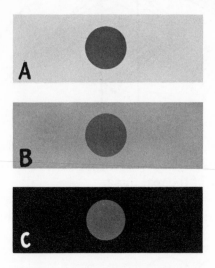

They are, of course, all the same tone of gray. The disc appears lighter when it is contrasted with a darker tone (figure C); the disc appears darker when it is contrasted with a lighter tone (figure A).

Even colored objects appear different in different surroundings. A green object, for example, may appear quite dark in a setting of light colors, and quite light in a setting of dark colors. If you have tried to match materials or paints, you know how a colored object is affected by surrounding colors.

The direction from which light comes will make a difference in how you see an object. We are accustomed to having light come from above us. Look at these two figures.

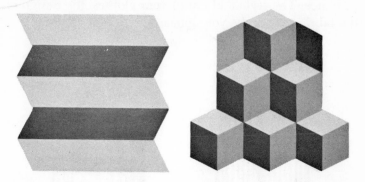

Which are the treads?   How many complete cubes
Which are the risers?   do you see, 3 or 6?

Turn the book upside down and look at the figures. With practice you can see the figures either way.

Here is an illusion that appears again and again on the printed page before you. Pick out any letter "s." Does the top of the letter appear to be the same size as the bottom? Is the bottom curve the same size as the top curve? Now turn the book upside down and look at the same letter. The bottom of the letter "s" is made larger because the eye sees the lower part more easily, more quickly. Since the upper part is seen more slowly, it would appear larger than the bottom part. By making the bottom part a little larger to begin with, the top and bottom of the letter appear to be the same size. A letter "s" with the smaller base would look unstable.

Illusions of seeing can help you to improve your appearance. The style and cut of your clothes, the design of the fabric may make you appear slimmer or stouter.

Which of the two men appears slimmer? Measure the width of the shoulders, neck, chest. Why does one appear slim, the other stout? The explanation lies in the way we see vertical and horizontal lines. Refer to the illustration at top of page 55.

To the eye more distant objects appear smaller. This is the illusion of perspective. For example, which of the two ladders is the longer?

To draw a scene in perspective means, therefore, to draw the objects in it as they appear to the eye rather than as they are. We would expect ladder B to be represented smaller because it is more distant from the eye.

Before the principle of perspective was discovered in art, about 500 years ago, painters represented the objects in a scene as they knew them to be rather than as they appeared to the eye. Such paintings appear flat and unreal. The illusion appears more natural.

Our eyes may fool us about the movement of things. Keep your eyes on the spiral for a few minutes. Does it appear to twirl?

The driver of a car is sometimes fooled in thinking that it is rolling when it is stopped. He has halted for a traffic light. As he looks out of the side window he has a feeling that his car is rolling. He jams his foot hard on the brake pedal. As he looks again out of the side window he realizes that his car had not rolled at all. It was the car alongside his that had done so.

You know that you are moving by seeing that objects

about you are either still or moving less rapidly than you are. Flying fast in an airplane above the clouds, where you can see neither the ground below nor the clouds above, you may have the illusion of being suspended in space, even though you may hear the roar of the plane's engines.

A motorist driving along a straight tarred road on a hot, clear day, may see what appears to be a wet spot on the road ahead. But when the car reaches the spot, it is dry, and another wet spot appears ahead.

This is a simple mirage. It is caused by the reflection of the the sky from a layer of heated air just above the road.

People who have traveled in deserts tell of remarkable mirages. Looking ahead on a hot, sun-baked desert, the traveler may suddenly see a lake and sheltering trees. He hastens toward it only to find that it is a mirage.

The hot sands of the desert heat the air just above it. The hot air expands and becomes lighter. Where it meets the cooler air just a few feet above the sands, a reflecting layer of air is formed. Rays of light from very distant objects are first refracted upward by the heated air, then reflected downward by the boundary of hot and cooler air. The traveler sees the reflected image as a mirage.

Mirages are sometimes seen at sea. Then the lighter, heated air is above the observer. He may see a weird, inverted image of distant objects, sometimes of objects below the horizon.

The many ways in which your eyes may fool you are optical illusions, illusions of seeing. You have yet to learn that seeing moving pictures and television broadcasts are also optical illusions.

5

SEEING RADIANT
ENERGY — COLOR

Light is radiant energy. So are X-rays and radio waves.

All kinds of radiant energy are alike in that they travel through the air as waves. They all move at the same tremendous speed of about 186 thousand miles a second.

The kinds of radiant energy differ from one another in the length and in the frequency of their waves. The length of a wave is measured from the crest — the highest point — of one wave to the crest of the next one. Frequency is the measure of the number of waves that pass a given point in a second. Since the speed — which is constant, remember — is the product of the wave length multiplied by the frequency, those forms of radiant energy with the shortest wave lengths have the highest frequency.

The different kinds of radiant energy may be arranged in a series, those with the shortest wave lengths at one end and those with the longest wave lengths at the other. This series is called the electromagnetic spectrum.

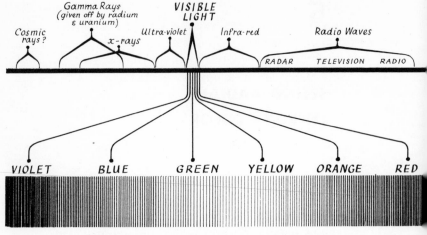

The Electromagnetic Spectrum, which includes
the narrow Light Spectrum (visible light)

The shortest wave lengths of this spectrum are the gamma rays, radiant energy given off by certain radioactive materials, such as uranium. Their wave lengths measure less than one hundred-millionth of an inch. These radiations have the highest frequency. The longest waves, at the other end of the spectrum, are the radio waves. They measure more than half a mile in length. In between, in increasing order of wave lengths, are X-rays, ultra-violet radiations, light waves, infra-red radiations, radar waves, and radio waves.

The arrangement of the waves of radiant energy in a spectrum may be thought of as a keyboard, like that of a piano with sixty keys. On such a keyboard the light spectrum, the visible electromagnetic waves, would be only one key. It is true that this one key is divided into a color spectrum made up of a range of frequencies, as you shall soon learn. But it is still a very small fraction of the total range of frequencies of the electromagnetic spectrum.

The shortest waves of the light spectrum are about 1/60,000 of an inch long. We see these waves as violet light. The longest waves of the light spectrum are about 1/30,000 of an inch long. We see these waves as red light. Wave lengths in between the shortest and the longest are seen as the other colors — blue, green, yellow, and orange. Electromagnetic waves that are shorter or longer than those of the light spectrum cannot be seen.

When all the wave lengths of the light spectrum enter the eye at the same time, in nearly equal quantities, we see the light as colorless or white. That is why sunlight or the light from an electric lamp appears colorless. Such light is, however, made up of all the colors of the light spectrum.

All white light is not of the same quality. That depends on the mixture of wave lengths that make up the light. For example, an electric light may appear white in a room at night. The same light in the same room will appear yellow in daylight. This means that the spectrum of the light from the electric lamp is different from the spectrum for sunlight. They are made up of different mixtures of colors, of different mixtures of visible radiant energy.

The colors in white light may be made visible with the help of a piece of glass, a glass prism. A beam of light from a flashlight may be passed through the prism. It comes out as a band of colors — red at one end, changing to orange,

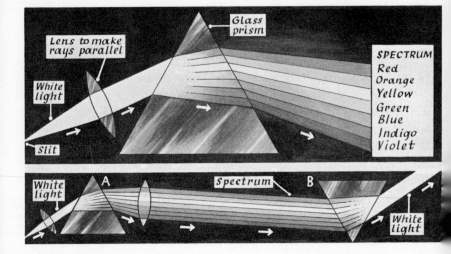

Diffraction of light in a triangular glass prism. White light is broken up into its constituent colors in Prism A; then the colors are combined in Prism B, resulting in white light

yellow, green, blue, and finally violet at the other end. This band of colors is the visible light spectrum.

The speed of the light waves is slowed as they pass from air into glass. And the different wave lengths that make up white light are slowed in different degrees. The light waves are therefore bent as they pass through the glass prism. And the wave lengths are bent in different degrees. The original beam of white light is thus separated into its constituent colors and it comes out as a color spectrum.

If a second prism is placed in the path of the color spectrum, it comes through as a beam of white light. The different wave lengths are bent in different degrees as they pass from dense glass to less dense air. As a result they mix to form white light.

Raindrops in the air may act as prisms. Sunlight passing through them is separated into its component wave lengths. The result is the familiar rainbow, a color spectrum on a grand scale.

White is not a color, but rather a mixture of colors. This is easily demonstrated. Cut a circle two to four inches in diameter from a piece of stiff, white cardboard. With paint or crayon, color equal segments red, green, and blue. Next put a pointed peg through the center of the card so that it may be spun, or draw a string through it so that it may be twirled, as shown in the drawing. If the card is spun or twirled very fast, the colors mix. The card appears white.

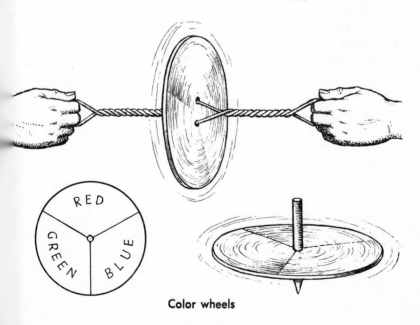

Color wheels

The three colors — red, green, and blue — are called primary colors. Mixed in equal parts they make white light. Other mixtures of these colors may be made to match almost all colors. Try different mixtures on the spinning or twirling card.

Light enters the eyes as a mixture of different wave lengths of radiant energy. The eyes cannot select for seeing any particular waves and shut out other waves. For example, the eyes cannot select only waves of green light from white light and see only the green parts of a scene.

Your radio or television set can be "tuned." When you tune it you select a particular wave length from among the many that are in the air. You thereby keep out of your receiving set other radio waves, so that you can hear or see a particular program without interference from other programs. The eyes have no tuner.

There is a saying about looking at the world through rose-colored glasses. It is supposed to make everything look "rosy," good. When you look through a real piece of rose-colored glass or cellophane at a scene of many colors, everything looks red, gray, or black. What becomes of the other colors?

The red glass passes through to the eyes only the red waves of light. The waves of other colors are stopped, absorbed, by the red glass. We say that the red glass filters the light. The filter acts as a tuner for light.

A green filter passes only the waves of green light. A blue filter passes only the waves of blue light. A filter passes through waves of a part of the color spectrum, absorbs all the others.

Color filters are used in making color snapshots, color

movies, color television. The color film in your camera has three layers. The top layer is sensitive only to blue light. A filter then stops these waves from passing to the next two layers. The middle layer is sensitive to green but not to red light. The lowest layer is sensitive to red light waves. Making a film layer sensitive to only one color is like filtering white light.

Thus three different color pictures are taken at the same time. One picture records the blue color of the scene or subject; one picture records the green color; one picture records the red color. When the film is developed, three different color images are produced, one on top of the other. We see them as a single image, in the original colors. Later you will learn how filters are used in making color television.

The surfaces of colored objects behave like color filters. Light from the sun or from an electric lamp shines on a red vase, for example. The surface of the vase absorbs all the wave lengths of the color spectrum except the red. Red rays are reflected to the eyes and the vase is seen as red. A green bowl next to the red vase will absorb all wave lengths except the green, which it will reflect. The bowl will be seen as green.

Suppose, now, a green light shines on a red vase. What will be the color of the vase as we see it? The surface of the vase absorbs the green light, reflects no light. Under a green light a red vase will appear to be black.

When we say that an object is a particular color, we mean that the object reflects that color. The color that the object reflects depends upon the color of its surface and upon the quality of the light that shines upon the surface.

For example, the spectrum of colors that makes up

a tungsten-wire electric lamp is quite different from the spectrum of a fluorescent light. And the spectrum of both of these lights is different from that of sunlight. The quality of light depends on the mixture of wave lengths that comprise it.

Moreover, the spectrum of daylight will vary at different times during the day. Early and late in the day it has more red in it. That explains the rosy glow of mountain peaks or of tall buildings at daybreak, the flame-colored glow of a sunset. It explains, also, why the faces of friends whose pictures you took on color film in the late afternoon look so red.

Have you ever tried to match the color of a tie, or of a scarf, or of a dress under an electric light in a store? Were you surprised when you later looked at the match in the daylight?

The cones in the retina enable us to see color, as you know. They are connected to a network of nerves. Most scientists believe that this network is made up of three different systems. One system is sensitive to the radiations for red light; one is sensitive to the radiations for green light; one is sensitive to radiations for blue light. This is like the sensitive layers in color film.

The three systems of nerves must overlap in their sensitivity. In this way we are able to see all the colors of the spectrum. The nerves and the brain are able to change the waves of radiant energy into color sensations.

A scientist has now shown that color can be seen from black and white pictures of colored objects. He took two pictures of the same colored objects on black and white film. One picture was taken through a red filter, a second one was taken without a filter. The camera was held in the same position for both pictures.

After the films were developed he projected the two pictures on a screen, one on top of the other, so that they overlapped and matched exactly. The first picture was projected through a red filter, the second one was projected directly. The picture on the screen was seen in colors, like the original one.

This may well mean that seeing color does not depend on special nerve networks that are each sensitive to a particular wave length of radiant energy. The wave lengths of light are not, according to this experiment, the color makers. The longer wave lengths (red) and the shorter wave lengths (green and blue) appear to act upon one another. The results of this interaction are reflected to the eyes.

The eyes and the brain are somehow able to interpret the results and to assign to each object, or to each part of each object, its proper color. The experiments of this scientist suggest that seeing color is much more complicated than taking color pictures in a camera. This emphasizes once again the fact that seeing is a mental process.

The mind interprets the color of an image that the retina transmits to the brain, just as the mind fills in details in an image. Thus, if you were buying a colored scarf, you might take it to the store window to see its color by daylight. You form a mental image of its color. Thereafter it will always appear to you to have this color, regardless of the quality of the light that illuminates it. We tend to remember the colors of objects, so that we do not look at the objects themselves too closely.

Many people, about one in twelve, are color blind. Mostly men are affected, and usually they are born that way. That is to say, it is an inherited condition that affects the development in such a way as to impair the ability to see certain colors. It may be the cones, the nerve connections, or even the interpretive center in the brain that is imperfectly developed.

There are many kinds and degrees of color blindness. Some color blind people see one part of the color spectrum as gray. More commonly they may have difficulty in telling one color from another — red from green, for example. These people would have trouble driving a car in the city where there are traffic lights, although color blind people may differentiate traffic lights by their position. In most cases the color blindness is slight, and in all cases the vision is normal in other respects.

Radiant energy with wave lengths just beyond the light spectrum, on either side, may be used to make things visible, even though the radiations are themselves invisible.

Just beyond the red end of the light spectrum are radiations called infra-red. They can pass through the haze of the atmosphere that stops light waves. Infra-red radiations can be focused by a camera lens. They produce photochemical changes on film that has been made sensitive to these radiations. Pictures can then be taken through a red filter which will show clear details of scenes which cannot be seen by the eyes, because of mist or fog.

Just beyond the violet end of the light spectrum there are electromagnetic radiations called ultra-violet. Certain minerals glow when exposed to them. Objects may be coated with paints made with such minerals. These objects are

Left side photographed on normal film; right side on film
made sensitive to infrared radiations, through a red filter

then exposed to lamps that are covered with filters so that they emit no visible radiations. In a completely dark room, with no visible illumination, the objects are made visible as they glow under invisible radiations.

In the theatre ultra-violet radiations are sometimes used to produce startling effects. Dancers wear costumes covered with dyes that glow under these radiations. When all the house and stage lights are turned off, the costumes are seen dancing about, but the dancers are not seen.

The dyes in the costumes, as the paints mentioned above, absorb the invisible ultra-violet radiations and return some of them to the eyes as visible radiations.

It is radiant energy that triggers the photochemical changes in the rods and cones. The different wave lengths of visible radiant energy enable the cones to see color. While we do know some of the story of how the eye sees, we do not know how the photochemical changes result in color sensations, or how the mind interprets the color sensations.

6

REFLECTION, REFRACTION, DIRECTION OF LIGHT WAVES

Several thousand years ago, according to the myth, there lived in ancient Greece a very handsome youth named Narcissus. He was loved by many fair maidens, but he could love no one of them. He even spurned the love of the very fair Echo. For love of him she pined away until there was nothing left of her but her voice.

The Goddess Nemesis plotted to avenge the lovelorn maidens. One day, as Narcissus sat beside a fountain, he looked down into the pool of water. He saw there a beautiful face with which he fell in love. He could not, of course, have this love. So he pined away and he was changed into a flower that bears his name to this day.

The myth isn't altogether clear. Did Narcissus think that the face was that of a water nymph who always eluded him? His mother was a water nymph. Or did he, as most people believe, fall in love with his own image which he saw by reflection in the pool?

Psychologists use the myth of Narcissus to describe a person who loves himself so much that he cannot love any other. The story is of interest to us because it is based on the reflection of light waves.

Light, as you know, travels through space as waves of electromagnetic energy. These waves are spherical in form. You will understand this if you think of a street light at a corner intersection. You see the light when you look up at it. You would also see it if you were to look down on it from a neighboring rooftop. You can see it from the East,

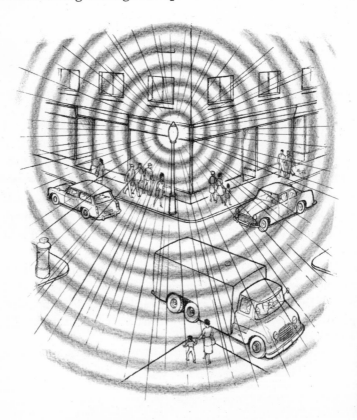

A light wave has a spherical wave front

from the West, from the North, from the South, and from all points of the compass in between.

If we were to select a point on the advancing wave front, and follow it, we would see that it makes a straight line. Moreover, the front of the wave flattens as it advances. The line made by a point on the front may be called a light ray.

We cannot make a drawing of a spherical wave front to show how it behaves. Hence the drawings in this book, or in any book about light, show light rays. But what is true of one ray of the light wave is true of the infinite number of rays that make up an advancing light wave.

Now when you hear that light travels in a straight line you understand that it is the light rays that do so. The light wave travels continuously in the same direction. But its direction may be changed.

What happens when light waves strike a surface? That depends on the nature of the surface and on the nature of the light waves. White light striking a surface may be absorbed in part or in whole. You already know that we see colored objects as a result of their absorption of part of the light that falls upon them. If the light were totally absorbed, the object could not be seen. If the surface were totally black, we could not see it.

Light waves pass through a pane of glass with very little loss. A little is absorbed, a little is reflected. A transparent surface transmits light waves. The direction of the light waves will change somewhat as they pass into and through the glass. You will soon know the reason.

If the surface is shiny like a mirror, or like that of a polished nickel- or chromium-plated object, the light waves will be reflected. They will bounce back. How they do so depends on the angle at which they strike the reflecting surface.

Standing before a mirror is not an unusual experience for you. You do so when you adjust your tie or clothing, comb your hair, shave, apply makeup, or do the many other things that good grooming or your vanity impel you to do.

Your image in the mirror is erect. It appears to be the same distance behind the mirror that you are in front of it. It is, moreover, symmetrical. That is, the left side of the image is your left side, so that you and your image could overlap.

But you do not see the image as a result of light waves that it sends to your eyes. Nor could you catch it on a card or a screen. A mirror image is called "virtual" in contrast to a real image which we see as a result of the light waves that it reflects to our eyes. Narcissus saw a virtual image.

We see only a very small portion of any spherical light wave. That small portion, a single light ray, or a group of light rays, travels in a straight line. Light rays or waves do not bend around corners. That is why you cannot see over the heads of people standing in front of you at a football game, or at a parade. But the direction of light waves can be changed, not only once, but many times, to enable you to do so.

If light waves strike a surface at an angle, they bounce off at an angle. The angle at which they strike the surface is called the angle of incidence. The angle at which they

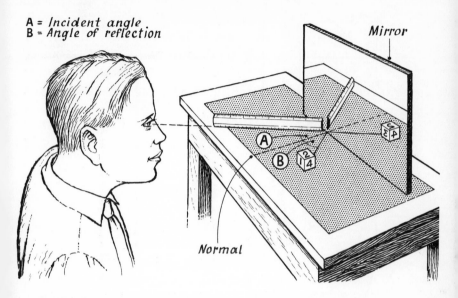

A = *Incident angle*
B = *Angle of reflection*

Mirror

Normal

are reflected is called the angle of reflection. The basic law of reflection is this: the angle of reflection is equal to the angle of incidence. These angles are like those made by a ball when you bounce it to a friend. If you can estimate angles well by sight, you throw the ball so that it strikes the ground at an angle that will make it bounce into the hands of your friend on the rebound.

Using this principle you can make a simple periscope (this word means to see around something) which will enable you to see over heads and around corners. You use two flat mirrors set at an angle of 45 degrees, mounted in

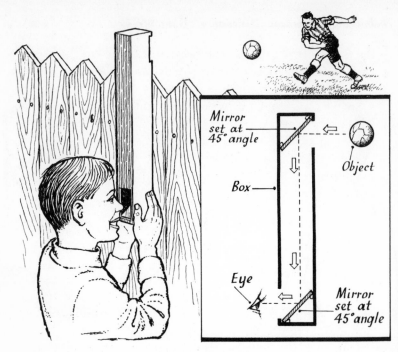

Mirror set at 45° angle

Box

Object

Eye

Mirror set at 45° angle

A mirror periscope

a tube as shown in the diagram. Follow the light rays on the diagram to see how they are reflected to the eye so that you may see an image.

Glass prisms may also be used to reflect light rays. They do so more efficiently than do mirrors because there is no loss of light because of absorption. You will read later how prisms act as reflectors.

We use flat, plane mirrors mostly. But mirrors may have spherical surfaces. Take for example, the small mirror attached to an automobile just outside the window next to the driver. It is called a rear view mirror. It has a convex surface. When he looks at it the driver has a view of the road behind him for quite a distance.

Such a convex mirror forms a small image of a large area. This image is erect, symmetrical, and virtual, like that in a plane mirror. But it is very much reduced in size.

Light rays are reflected from the surface of a convex mirror according to the same principle that applies to plane mirrors. However, the reflected rays are spread, diverged, because of the curvature of the surface.

Mirrors with concave surfaces are used more commonly, and they have more important uses than do those with convex surfaces. For example, the small mirror that the dentist uses in your mouth is concave. The largest telescopes use concave mirrors rather than convex lenses to magnify images of the distant stars. They are used, also, as reflectors in automobile headlights and in searchlights.

Concave mirrors concentrate, pinch together, light rays. The image that is produced depends on the distance of the object from a point called the principal focus, a point half way from the surface of the mirror to its center of curvature.

When the object or source of light is distant, as is a star, the rays of light from it will be focused at the principal focus of the mirror. The image will be real, small, and inverted. This is the telescope image.

If the object is placed closer to the mirror than its principal focus, the image will be large, erect, and virtual. This is the image in the dentist's mirror, or in a shaving mirror.

When a light is placed at the principal focus of a con-

The concave reflector in each of these 800-million-
candlepower searchlights produces a straight beam
of light that has an effective range of 21 miles

cave mirror, the light rays are reflected as a straight beam of
light. This is how the concave mirror is used in an automobile headlight or in a searchlight.

Shiny surfaces change the direction of light rays by reflection. This page also does so, but it reflects the rays diffusely. This means that the surface of the paper is quite un-
even and rough. If you examined its surface under a microscope, you would see an infinite number of crests and de-
pressions. Each of these reflects light rays in a different di-

rection, diffusely. That is why you can read the words on this page. If it were very smooth a glare would be reflected to your eyes. That makes it difficult to read matter printed on glossy paper.

Light waves pass more readily through some materials than they do through others. That is to say, the velocity of the waves is greater in some materials than it is in others. Those in which the velocity is reduced are called "optically dense." The greater the density, the greater the reduction in velocity. Thus, light passes more readily through air than it does through water; it passes more readily through water than it does through glass; more readily through glass than it does through a diamond.

When light rays pass from a less dense to a more dense material, they are slowed up. If the rays enter at right angles to the surface of the denser material, you do not see any change. If, however, the rays enter at any other angle, they are bent, their direction is changed. You have seen the optical illusion of a spoon that appears to bend at the water line in a glass of clear water. In passing from a less dense into a more dense material, light rays are bent toward the normal.

Think of a beam of light made up of many light rays passing from air into water. When they pass in at right angles to the surface of the water, they are all slowed up at the same time, to the same extent, and there is no change in the direction of the beam. If it enters the water at any other angle, some rays will enter before others and be slowed up, while the others move forward at the normal velocity. As a result the beam is bent. The effect is like the wheeling

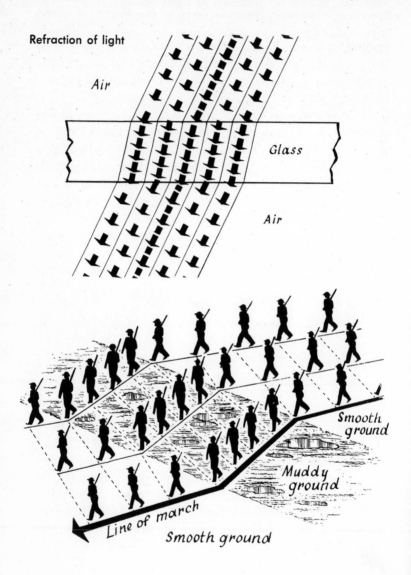

Refraction of light

Air

Glass

Air

Smooth ground

Muddy ground

Line of march

Smooth ground

maneuver of a line of marching men. When the entire beam or wave front has entered the water, there is no further change in the direction of the light rays. They are all moving at the same velocity.

The change in direction, the bending of light rays as they pass into a material of different optical density, is called refraction. The amount that the incident rays are refracted may be shown by a ratio, a relationship between the velocity of the incident rays and that of the refracted rays. It is shown like this:

$$\frac{\text{velocity of light in air}}{\text{velocity of light in other material}}$$

The amount of refraction may also be expressed as a ratio between the incident and refracted angles.

This ratio is called the index of refraction. Thus, if the index of air is 1, the index of water is 1.37; of glass 1.45-2.0 (depending on the purity of the glass); of diamond 2.45.

When light passes from a denser to a less dense material, the refracted rays are bent away from the normal. As the angle of incidence is increased, a point is reached where the incident ray cannot be refracted. This is the critical angle. Any increase in the angle of incidence results in reflection of the rays from the surface.

Every substance through which light passes has its critical angle. It is 48.5 degrees for water; a little less than 45 degrees for common glass; about 36 degrees for optical glass used in making lenses for spectacles, microscopes, and telescopes.

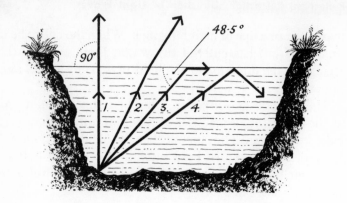

Direction of light rays: (1) unchanged;
(2) and (3) refracted; (4) totally reflected

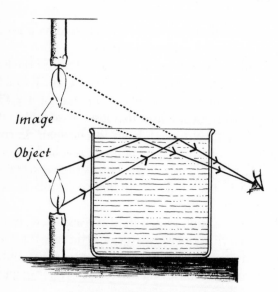

Image resulting from total reflection.

This kind of reflection explains how prisms are used as reflectors. If a beam of light is made to pass through the short side of a right angle prism (angles of 45-45-90 degrees) so that it strikes the long side of the prism at an angle greater than 36 degrees (for a prism made of optical glass) the beam will be totally reflected, as you now know.

Prisms are used in the periscopes of submarines because the light rays are totally reflected by them. There is no loss of light by absorption, as there is in mirrors. Prisms are used in binocular field glasses, as shown in the diagram. You see that the light is reflected four times, passes through the binocular tube three times. The advantage of using a prism binocular is that we can use a shorter tube to magnify a distant object. To get the same magnification with a telescope we should have to use a very much longer tube.

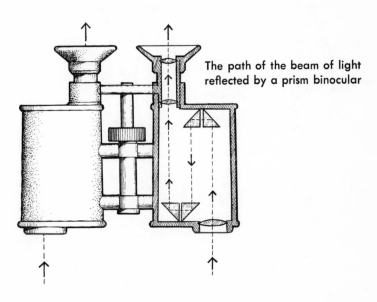

The path of the beam of light reflected by a prism binocular

Several rays of light entering a glass prism are refracted toward its base. The rays near the apex are refracted more than those near the base. Now think of two equal prisms, base to base. Rays of light directed toward them will be directed toward the bases. As a result such a lens converges, draws together, the rays of light. Such lenses are used to magnify objects.

A concave lens may be thought of as two equal prisms placed so that their apexes touch. Rays of light directed toward such a lens will also be refracted toward their bases.

Convex Lens   Concave Lens

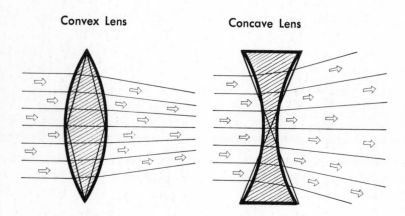

Lenses act like triangular glass prisms;
they refract rays of light toward the bases

As a result, the concave lens will diverge, spread, the rays of light. A concave lens will produce a reduced image.

You learn how the refraction of light by lenses is used when you read about the use of the lens of the eye in seeing; the use of lenses to correct sight; the use of lenses in microscopes to magnify objects;the use of lenses in telescopes to see distant objects; the use of a lens in a camera to take a picture and in a projector to show an image of the picture on a screen.

You know now that light travels continuously in one direction, unless that direction is changed by reflection or by refraction. You know the law of reflection: that the angle of reflection is equal to the angle of incidence. You know the law of refraction: the incident angle is changed in proportion to the change of velocity of the light in the other medium.

Light will enter a transparent plastic tube or rod and come out at the other end, regardless of the number of bends and twists in the tube. However, no bend or twist may be greater than the critical angle of the plastic. So long as the bend is less than the critical angle, the light will be reflected internally until it comes out at the other end. Such tubes have been used to illuminate the inside of a stomach, for example, so that a surgeon may examine it by sight.

A more flexible tube has been made like a cable, made up of hundreds, even thousands of thin, transparent plastic tubes. It works on the same principle as the thicker tube. The twists and bends in the cable must not exceed the critical angle of the plastic. An image of an illuminated object can be produced by this plastic cable. It will resemble the mosaic image of an insect's eye.

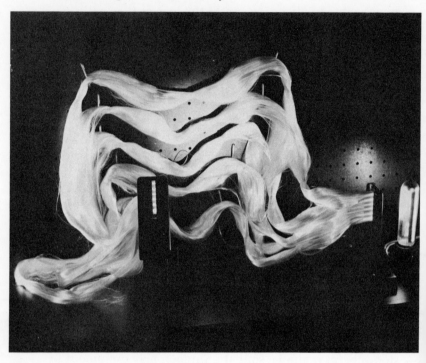

Plastic fibers of a plastic cable

7

SEEING THE UNSEEN
— THE MICROSCOPE

A drop of water from a stagnant pond is a teeming micro-cosm, a little world of hustling, bustling, living things. In this droplet pool hundreds of animals may swim about — feeding, breathing, working, growing, reproducing. Tiny green plants are the food of most of these animals. But some of them are carnivores — they eat other tiny animals.

But you would not see any of this life as you look at the drop of water. These animals and plants belong to a world too small to be seen by our eyes without help. Science has supplied the help, one of the most valuable tools of science, the microscope.

Microscope means to "see little things." The development of this instrument began far back in history when some man discovered that a thick, curved piece of glass magni-fied an object seen through it. There is, of course, no record to tell us who made this discovery, nor when or where it was made.

Two drops of stagnant water seen through a microscope. Top:
One-celled animals. Bottom: One-celled plants and tiny worms

Nor is there any record of who made the first lens. But we do know that magnifying glasses, lenses, were used by scientists at least 2,000 years ago.

Spectacles, lenses for seeing better, were in common use in many parts of Europe by the year 1500. It was a spectacle maker in Holland, Janssen by name, who is generally given credit for the invention of the microscope, about the year 1600.

The first ones were quite crude. They did not magnify greatly and they were mostly used as toys, to look at small insects, for example, such as fleas. The first microscopes were, indeed, often called "flea glasses."

Scientists and many self-educated laymen soon began to use microscopes seriously to look into the unseen world about them. They examined a great variety of things, and made one amazing discovery after another. They were exploring a hitherto unknown, unseen world.

Among the most notable of the early microscopists was a Dutchman, Anton van Leeuwenhoek. A self-taught man, without higher academic learning or scientific training, his studies with his microscopes earned him admission as a member to the learned Royal Society of London.

Leeuwenhoek designed and made hundreds of microscopes and ground as many fine lenses for them. His instruments were, to be sure, simple, even crude. His lenses were little more than large beads of glass. But they were very finely ground, so that many of them magnified a hundred times or more. One such lens may still be seen that magnifies 270 times.

For about 50 years, until his death in 1723 at the age of

Anton van Leeuwenhoek
with one of his
primitive microscopes

91, Leeuwenhoek sent a stream of letters to the Royal Society of London and to the French Academy of Science. In these letters he described the many observations and discoveries he made with his microscopes. There were nearly 500 such letters.

Leeuwenhoek is credited with many important first discoveries. Those that are included here are just a sampling to show the variety of his interests. He was the first to describe red blood corpuscles, and he proved that arteries and veins are linked by capillaries. He studied and first des-

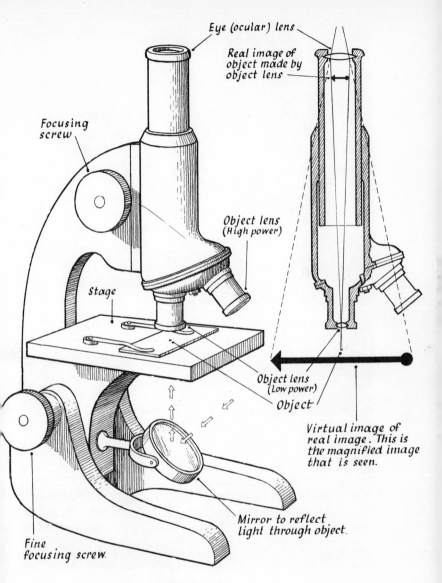

Eye (ocular) lens

Real image of object made by object lens

Focusing screw

Object lens (High power)

Stage

Object lens (Low power)

Object

Virtual image of real image. This is the magnified image that is seen.

Mirror to reflect light through object.

Fine focusing screw.

HOW A COMPOUND MICROSCOPE MAGNIFIES

MODERN MICROSCOPES

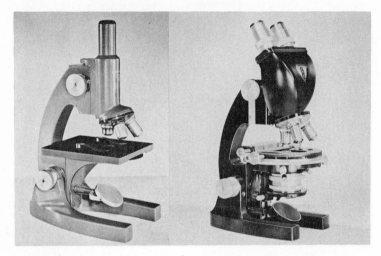

Student microscope

Medical research microscope

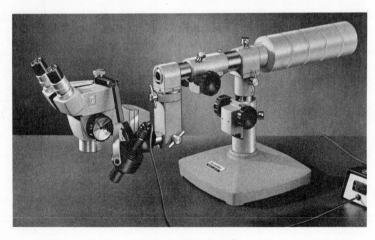

Surgical microscope

cribed sperm cells and the process of fertilization in a number of animals. He described the structure of muscle, of dental bone, of the lens of the eye. He first described and pictured bacteria, and many of the one-celled animals in stagnant water.

Microscope makers soon found that they could get greater magnification by using two lenses, one placed at either end of a tube. One lens was placed near the object so that it became known as the object lens. The eye was placed near the other lens and it became known as the ocular (eye) lens. Thus the compound microscope was invented. But it was still a rather simple instrument.

Studies and discoveries with microscopes went on, but the microscopes were improved but little until about the year 1850. Then began the changes and improvements in design that have produced the modern research microscope. See how the microscope has developed from its crude beginning!

How does a microscope magnify? To understand it, we must start with the simplest microscope, a single lens.

A lens that magnifies is convex. That is, it bulges in the middle, tapers or thins out to the edge, like a lentil seed. Hold such a lens so that the rays of sunlight pass through it. You see that the lens converges, gathers, the rays and brings them to a point. To do this the lens must bend the rays of light. Those near the edge are bent more than those near the center. This is refraction.

The distance from the center of the lens to the point where all the rays come to a point is called the focal length of the lens. With strong light such as sunlight the point of focus may become so hot that a piece of wood may be set on fire. For this reason convex lenses have been called "burning glasses."

Any other light source may be used to find the focal length of a lens. For example, we may do so for a more con-

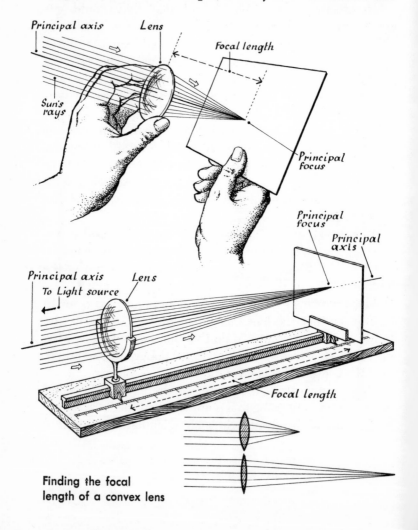

Finding the focal
length of a convex lens

vex (thicker in the center) lens and for a less convex lens, as in the illustration. The light is placed at some distance from the lens. Measure the distance from the lens to the focus. The more convex lens has the shorter focal length. The less convex lens has the longer focal length.

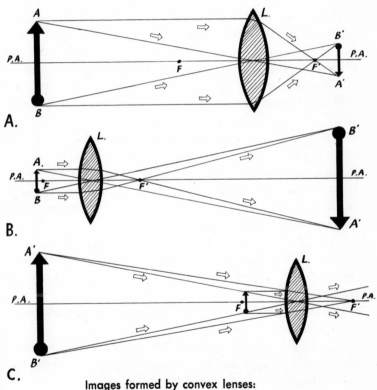

Images formed by convex lenses:
(A) Object quite far from the focus of the lens
(B) Object a little beyond the focus of the lens
(C) Object closer to the lens than its focus

Now we may see how convex lenses magnify. Suppose we place the object we wish to examine at a distance from the lens that is less than its focal length. Looking through the lens we see: (1) an enlarged image; (2) the image is right side up; (3) the image appears to be on the same side of the lens as the object; (4) the more convex lens (with the shorter focal length) shows the greater image, magnifies more.

If the object is placed at a distance from the lens that is greater than its focal length then: (1) The image is enlarged; (2) the image cannot be seen through the lens but it can be projected on a screen; (3) the image is upside down and reversed; (4) the image appears on the opposite side of the lens from the object. This kind of image is called "real" because it can be seen on a screen.

This is how an enlarged image is produced by a slide or a moving picture projector. The picture is placed in the projector upside down and reversed. It is placed at a distance from the projector lens that is greater than its focal length, but near its focus; the image comes out on the screen right side up and greatly enlarged.

The rays of light are bent, refracted, as they pass from the air into the glass. They are refracted more from the outer part of the lens than they are near the center. They are refracted more by a more convex lens than by a less convex lens. The size of the image depends on the degree of refraction.

The diagrams show how the lenses change the direction of the rays of light that are reflected from the object (the arrow) to produce enlarged images.

There are, of course, any number of light rays that are reflected from the object to the lens, from every point on the object. The diagrams show only those rays that are necessary to explain how the image is formed.

Thus A and A′ are parallel rays of light that pass from either end of the object to the lens, where they are refracted. B and B′ are rays that originate at the same points as A and A′ respectively, but pass through the center of the lens. They are refracted but not bent because at this point the portions of the lens through which they pass are parallel. The eye looking through the lens sees rays A and B, and A′ and B′ meet at 1 to form an image.

In a compound microscope, one lens is placed near the object at a distance greater than its focal length. This object lens has a short focal length so that it magnifies greatly. It produces an enlarged image that is upside down. The image appears to be in the tube.

The second, the ocular (eye) lens, enlarges the first image. We see the second image. Thus, if the first lens magnifies the tiny object 10 times, and the second lens magnifies the first image 10 times, you see an image that is magnified 100 times.

This is the principle upon which all microscopes work. Instead of a single lens at either end of the tube, better microscopes have a set of lenses. The combinations of lenses not only give greater magnification, but correct certain defects of lenses.

Have you noticed in looking through a lens that the image is clearest in the center, less clear around the edges? You may often see this in photographs taken with inexpensive cameras. Images seen or pictures taken through the center of a lens are clearest. This defect of lenses is due to their spherical surface.

You may have noticed, too, in using a magnifying glass, a rainbow around the edge of the image. As a result the image is less clear around the edge. This defect of lenses is due to the quality of the glass.

The combination of lenses used in microscopes near the object and near the eye is designed to correct these defects and thus give very clear images.

Microscopes may have two, three and sometimes four object lenses mounted on a pivot, so that any one of them may be used in combination with the eye lens. Each of the object lenses has a different focal length. The lens with the longest focal length is called the low power lens; that with the shortest focal length is the high power lens. Naturally, the higher the power, the greater the magnification.

Microscopes are most often used to examine transparent objects. Light passes up through the object, through the tube, to the eye. The light may be reflected through it by a mirror, or it may be passed up directly from the light source. Lenses with great magnifying power need consid-

Seen through a microscope: (A) Shells of one-celled animals such as make up chalk; (B) a string of one-celled plants; (C) nerve cells from the spinal cord of an animal; (D) cells in a pine needle; (E) salacine crystal; (F) a chick embryo 72 hours old

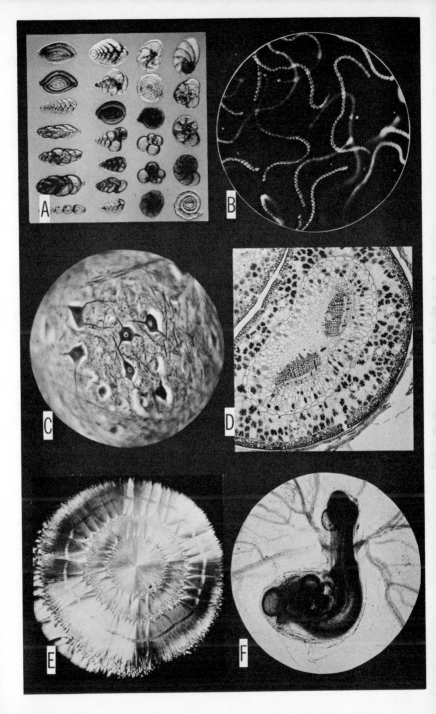

erable illumination. For this reason, the light is passed through a condensing lens to concentrate it on the object.

Microscopes are made which can examine solid objects such as minerals and industrial materials. Since they are not transparent, light must shine down on them. Such a microscope has been designed to help in crime detection. It compares the marking, as seen under the microscope, made by the firing pin of a pistol with the marking on a bullet that was fired in a crime. In this way the gun that was used in the crime may be identified.

With most microscopes you look at the object with only one eye. Thus you see a flat picture. Some microscopes have double eyepieces, called binocular eyepieces. Such microscopes give stereo, 3-D, vision. The image appears to have three dimensions, depth as well as length and breadth.

For example, if you look at a box-shaped object with a monocular, single eye lens, microscope, it will appear flat. The binocular microscope will show it as a box. The object lenses of binocular microscopes are of relatively long focal length. Hence these microscopes do not magnify greatly.

A binocular microscope has been designed that enables surgeons to perform very delicate operations on the inner ear, the parts of which are very tiny. With the binocular microscope the surgeon sees the parts clearly, enlarged, and in their actual relation to one another. He can therefore operate successfully where it would be extremely difficult without the help of the binocular microscope.

Using very fine lenses and strong light on the objects, scientists are able to magnify them as many as 2,000 times.

Thus they have discovered many of the very tiny germs that cause disease. By studying them and learning their habits scientists have been able to control many of them.

They have discovered, too, that plants and animals are made up of tiny parts called cells. By studying the structure of these cells, they have learned a great deal about how living things work. As a result they are often able to help when something goes wrong.

However, microscopes with glass lenses that use light to illuminate the object have a limited magnification. The limit is set by the wave length of light. An object that is smaller than half the average wave length of light (1/90,000 of an inch) cannot be seen through a light-illuminated microscope. Moreover, if two objects or structures in the specimen under examination are separated by a distance less than half the average wave length of light, they will not be seen as separate images.

Scientists, therefore, could not see many structures in cells either because they were too small, or because they were separated by too small distances. Nor could they see such small objects as the viruses that cause poliomyelitis (infantile paralysis), for example, nor could they see even quite large molecules.

The problem of seeing objects very much smaller than can be seen with an optical microscope has been solved to some extent. Scientists have designed a microscope that uses a form of radiation with a smaller wave length than that of visible light. This is the principle of the electron microscope.

A stream of electrons is used. They are given off from a

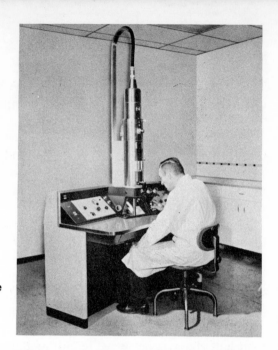

The electron microscope
and how it works

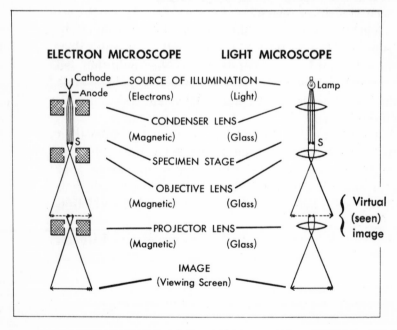

ELECTRON MICROSCOPE		LIGHT MICROSCOPE
Cathode Anode	SOURCE OF ILLUMINATION (Electrons)　　　　(Light)	Lamp
	CONDENSER LENS (Magnetic)　　　　(Glass)	
S	SPECIMEN STAGE	S
	OBJECTIVE LENS (Magnetic)　　　　(Glass)	
	PROJECTOR LENS (Magnetic)　　　　(Glass)	Virtual (seen) image
	IMAGE (Viewing Screen)	

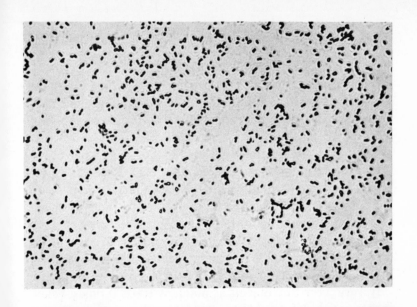

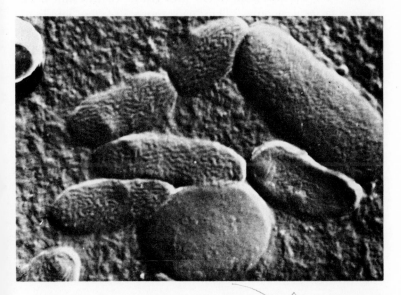

The same bacteria magnified (top) 1200 times by an optical microscope, and (below) 40,000 times by an electron microscope

cathode tube at 50,000 volts. Electrons are small, negatively charged particles. The stream of electrons takes the place of a beam of light. But the electrons behave like radiations with a wave length 1/50,000 that of the average wave length of light.

In using the electron microscope, the object to be examined is placed in a vacuum chamber. This is necessary because electrons would be deflected by the molecules in air. The electrons are focused on the object by means of magnets. A shadow picture of the object is projected on a screen that is like a television screen. That is, it glows when electrons strike it. The image may be photographed.

With an electron microscope it is possible to magnify very, very tiny objects as much as 100,000 times. Scientists are therefore able to see and study viruses and even some large molecules. They can, moreover, see details of structure in small objects, cells for example, that they could not see with optical microscopes.

The electron microscope adds another important tool that scientists can use to see farther into the unseen world of little things. But it too has its limitations. It is an expensive tool and requires great skill in use; but foremost is the fact that it cannot be used to study living cells.

Since the objects for examination must be placed in a vacuum tube, they must be dry or coated, sometimes with an extremely thin coat of a metal. Nonetheless, the electron microscope extends man's vision ever so much farther into the unseen world of very little things.

8

SEEING THROUGH THINGS—X-RAYS

You have surely had your picture taken by the use of light. Have you ever had one taken by X-rays? The first shows what you look like on the outside. The second would show what you look like on the inside.

Light and X-rays are alike in some ways. Both are forms of radiant energy. Both cause chemical changes in photographic films by means of which pictures are taken.

Light and X-rays are different in some ways. Light waves are 100 to 1000 times longer than the waves of X-rays. Light waves can be seen; X-rays cannot be seen. X-rays pass easily through many materials that stop or keep out light waves.

X-rays are produced in tubes like the one on page 110. At one end is an electron gun called the cathode. In line with the gun is a metal plate called the target. The gun and the target are sealed in a vacuum tube. That is, the air is removed from the tube so that very few stray atoms

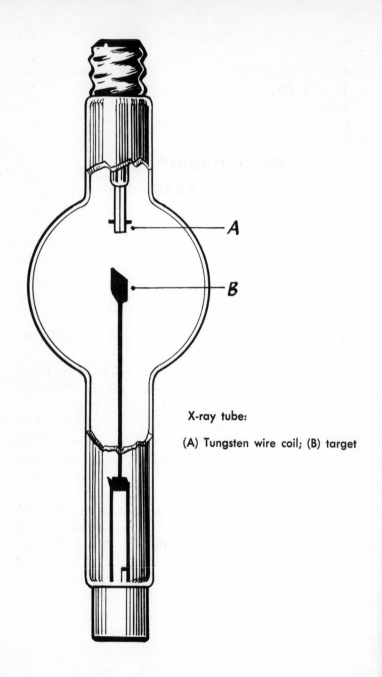

X-ray tube:

(A) Tungsten wire coil; (B) target

of air are left in it. Such atoms would deflect the electrons.

The source of electrons in the electron gun is a coil of tungsten wire, the same wire that there is in an electric lamp. When the coil of wire is heated white hot by electricity, it gives off a stream of electrons. The tube is connected to a powerful source of electricity. Currents as high as one million volts shoot the electrons at enormous speeds of many thousands of miles per second toward the target.

The speeding electrons strike the metal target. It is made of a metal that will withstand the heat that results from the bombardment by the stream of electrons. The bombardment causes a great disturbance of the atoms of the target. As a result, radiant energy is given off. The radiant energy is given off as X-rays.

The tube is shielded with lead, or leaded glass to prevent stray X-rays from escaping. X-rays cannot pass through lead if it is thick enough. The target is set so that the X-rays can pass out of the tube through an unshielded place, and only at that place. X-rays can be very harmful.

The higher the voltage of electricity used in producing the X-rays, the shorter is their wave length. The shorter the wave length, the greater is their power to pass through solid objects. They pass through some solid objects more easily than they do through others. For example, they pass more easily through wood than they do through metal.

Most of us become acquainted with X-rays when a dentist takes a picture of our teeth. In a lifetime, many of us may have X-ray pictures taken of other parts of our bodies.

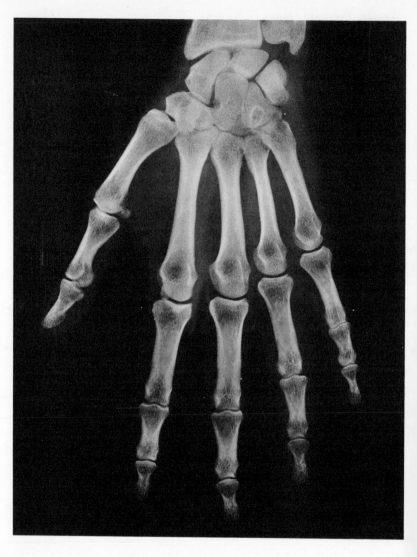

X-ray picture of hand and wrist

Doctors use X-rays to see through and into the body. To get a picture of the hand, for example, it is placed over a film in a light-proof wrapping. X-rays are then shot at the hand. They pass through the hand and through the light-proof wrapping. The film is developed like a picture taken with a camera. The result is a shadow picture, such as you see here. The bones appear light because the X-rays do not pass through them easily. The soft muscles, on the other hand, appear dark.

This picture is, of course, a negative. The places on the film where the least photochemical change took place are light. Where more photochemical change took place the negative is dark. The extent of photochemical change depends on how many X-rays reached that part of the film. The negative could be printed and a positive picture made, as is done with the film made with a camera. But the doctor does not need a positive picture. He can learn what he needs to know from the negative.

X-rays help a doctor to set a broken bone properly. He can locate a coin or other object that a child may have swallowed. Little stones that sometimes form in the kidneys or bladder may be located.

Even the soft parts of the body may be seen and studied by means of X-rays. Thus the doctor can see the size, position and action of the heart. He can learn about the condition of the lungs. A patient may be given a liquid to swallow that makes it possible for the doctor to see a clear outline of the stomach and the intestines. X-rays enable a doctor to diagnose many diseases.

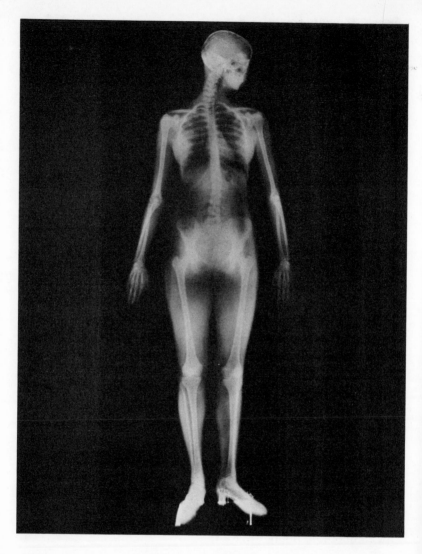

X-ray picture of the entire body

It isn't always necessary to take a picture to see into the body. Some chemicals glow when X-rays strike them and this glow is called fluorescence. A screen coated with such a chemical may be used instead of a film. The screen is held in front of the part of the body that the doctor wants to see. X-rays are passed through the part from behind it. The doctor sees a shadow picture on the screen. The screen is called a fluoroscope.

As mentioned before, X-rays can be very harmful. Large doses may cause injuries like severe burns. The damage may not appear for some time. Small doses given over a period of time may pile up to cause injury. Doctors who work with X-rays protect themselves by wearing aprons and gloves which are loaded with lead. They may stand behind heavily leaded screens. Scientists have warned that doctors must use X-rays with caution. A patient may suffer injury as a result of excessive exposure to them over a period of time.

X-rays destroy diseased tissues of the body more readily than they do healthy tissues. For this reason they are used in treating cancers that cannot be removed by surgery. X-ray treatment is often given, after a cancer has been removed by surgery, to destroy any diseased tissue that may not have been removed.

If you now have an idea that X-rays are used only by doctors, it will surprise you to learn some of the many uses of the rays in industry.

As X-rays pass through the crystals that make up different substances, they may produce "fingerprint photographs" that may be used to identify the different substances. For example, a real diamond will produce a different "fingerprint" from that of an imitation; a silk fiber will produce a different "fingerprint" from that of a nylon fiber. Thus X-rays enable us to extend our sight so that we may see the hidden structure of many substances.

House builders often need the help of X-rays. Plumbers have used them to locate the positions of pipes in the walls of old buildings. Electricians have used them to locate the position of wires in old walls. X-rays were used to discover the cause of the weakness of the roof beams of a cathedral in England. The rays showed the presence of many wood-boring beetles.

Probably the greatest use of X-rays in industry is in heavy metal construction. Metal frames of all kinds are now held together by welding rather than by bolts or rivets. Thus, automobile and airplane bodies, locomotives, steel cylinders, and building frames are welded. X-rays are the only means of testing a weld for weakness without destroying it. There are X-ray machines that can see through 10 inches of steel to discover cracks or patches.

X-rays are used, also, to examine manufactured products by seeing through them. Inspectors use the rays to see through aircraft instruments, electronic tubes, and other precision built products. Automobile tires are inspected with X-rays to see if the cord and the rubber are well united. Even rockets can be quickly inspected with the rays to see if they have been properly assembled.

These uses of X-rays in industry are samples of many. If

you are interested in detective stories you should know that
the police often use them to see into bundles and baggage
to look for hidden, illegal articles. Customs inspectors may
also use them for the same purpose.

Moving picture film

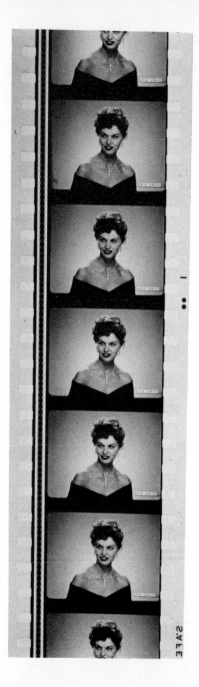

9

SEEING MOVING PICTURES

The strip of pictures at the left is a piece of moving picture film. But it looks like a series of still pictures. That's what it is, a series of snapshots. How can a series of still pictures become a moving picture?

To understand how they do so we must recall how we see. When the rays of light are reflected into the eyes they strike the rods and cones. Here they cause chemical changes. This results in nerve impulses. They pass to the brain where the image is seen.

The changes that are brought about in the rods and cones stay on the retina for a fraction of a second. We may say this another way. The retinal image produced by the rays of light persists for a fraction of a second. If a second image is formed on the retina before the first one fades out, the two images overlap. A third image will overlap the second; a fourth image will overlap the third; and so on.

If a series of overlapping images of a moving subject is formed on the retina, the brain sees the series as a moving picture. But the images must be formed on the retina at the rate of approximately 24 in a second. The secret of seeing moving pictures is this: Each picture must make a small change in the movement of the subject; the pictures must follow one another at the rate of about 24 a second.

Cartoon movies work on the same principle. Drawings are made which show successive movements of each character in the scene. The pictures are then photographed on a roll of film. When the pictures are projected on a screen, 24 in a second, the characters appear to move.

You can understand that many thousands of drawings must be made for a cartoon movie. The movements of each character in the scene are studied. The time that is needed to complete each movement is noted. The artist then makes the necessary number of drawings to show the movements on the screen in the given time. Think what this means if the characters in the cartoon speak! Then the number of drawings must fit the movements of the lips in speaking the words.

A moving picture camera really takes still pictures. But it takes them one after another, 24 in a second. (Silent, home movies are made at the rate of sixteen in a second.)

When the shutter of a moving picture camera opens a snapshot is taken in about 1/35 of a second. Then the shutter closes. The film, which is on a roll, is moved along the width of one picture. Each picture is called a "frame." The shutter opens again, and another picture is taken. Again the shutter closes and the film is moved along one frame. A motor moves the film and operates the shutter. The finished moving picture is a roll made up of thousands of frames, snapshots taken one after another.

After the roll of film is developed it must be projected on a screen. The moving picture projector has a shutter like the moving picture camera. It is operated by a motor so that it opens and closes 24 times in a second. The motor also moves the film along.

A bright light is placed behind the film. When the shutter is open, the light passes through it and is focused on the screen by the lens. The shutter is then closed and the next frame is moved in place in front of the light. This continues, so that 24 pictures are shown on the screen in a second.

When seeing a movie, you imagine that the pictures are on the screen continuously. This is because the retinal image of one picture persists until the next picture forms a retinal image. You imagine that the characters on the screen move. This is because the images succeed one another at the rate of 24 in a second.

If the projector is run very slowly, you see a series of still pictures. The images do not merge. If the film is run through the projector very quickly, the pictures on the screen blur. Each picture does not stay on the screen long enough for a clear retinal image to be formed.

If the projector is run at about half normal speed the characters on the screen move, but their movements are jerky. The effect is like seeing by the light of a sputtering candle. The reason for this is that the screen becomes dark for an instant between pictures, although not long enough to spoil completely the illusion of motion. The pictures on the screen appear to flicker. In the early days of the movies, when the cameras and the projectors did not operate so well, and there were fewer frames per second, moving pictures were often called "the flickers."

Many moving picture cameras, even inexpensive ones, can take as many as 64 pictures in a second. Suppose you you take them at the rate of 64 a second, but project them at the normal rate of 24 a second. The result on the screen is slow motion pictures. You have seen a high diver float slowly and gracefully through the air; the batter swing his bat with deliberate slowness to meet the ball which then floats slowly toward the outfield; the golfer swing his club to make a slow arc, strike the ball, which then floats into the air. One can improve one's form in a sport by studying the movements in slow motion.

There are cameras that can take as many as 2,000 pictures in a second. They are then projected at the normal rate of 24 a second. The result on the screen is ultra-slow motion. Such moving pictures are very useful in industry, for example, in studying the work of speeding parts of an engine; in studying the action of a missile as it blasts off.

On the other hand, we can speed up action on the screen. Have you ever seen a flower bud burst into full bloom on the screen in a few seconds? The original action may have taken several hours, or even days. Single pictures are taken at regular intervals of time while the sub-

Frames from an ultra-slow motion picture
showing a drop falling into a glass of milk

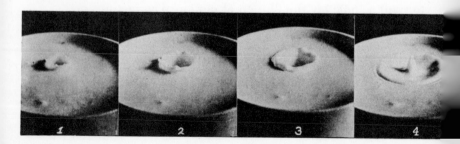

ject and the camera are kept in fixed positions. Thus, one picture may be taken every minute for six hours. When the pictures are projected on the screen at the rate of 24 a second, the action will take fifteen seconds. Such pictures are called time-lapse moving pictures. There is a lapse of time between the taking of successive pictures.

Moving pictures seen on a screen at home appear flat, as indeed they are. In a theater they often appear stereoscopic, so that they appear to have depth as well as width and height. Such movies appear more realistic.

In the theatre the moving pictures are shown on screens that are not only wider in proportion to the home screen, but are curved at both sides as well. If you study the pictures shown on such a wide screen, you see that the people and objects in the center of the screen are seen more clearly than those at the sides.

The center of the picture on the screen is focused on the cones of the fovea of the retina. These cones, you will remember, enable you to see most clearly. The sides of the picture are focused on other cones and on rods. You see the people and the objects on the sides less clearly. But because you see them at all, the whole picture has a more "real" look, a stereoscopic look.

Seeing still pictures move is an illusion, an optical illusion.

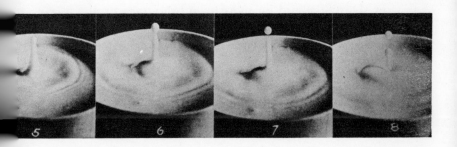

10

SEEING ACROSS SPACE
— TELEVISION

Imagine sitting in comfort in a room at home watching a football game being played 3,000 miles away! At another time you may become a spectator at an historic meeting of the United Nations. Television has made it possible to see across space.

Sending a television program across space starts off like taking a moving picture. Rays of light reflected from the scene enter the television camera. They pass through a lens, as they do in a moving picture camera. From this point, telecasting is different from movie making.

Inside the television camera there is an electronic tube somewhat wider at one end. This is an iconoscope — a television camera image tube. Such tubes have been improved: for sensitivity to light; for the production of images of greater sharpness; and for more even brightness on the receiving screens. Such improved tubes are the image-orthicons, but in principle they work like the original iconoscope that is described here.

An image-orthicon tube

How an iconoscope
forms the image

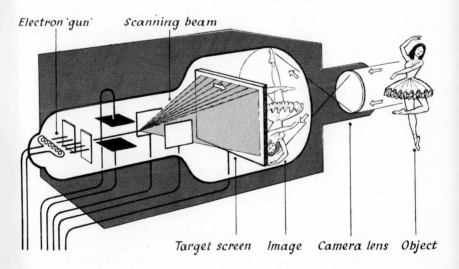

Electron gun   *Scanning beam*

Target screen   *Image*   *Camera lens*   *Object*

The light rays from the subject before the television camera are focused on a screen at the wider front end of the tube. This screen takes the place of the film in the camera that you use to take pictures. On this screen there are thousands of tiny, invisible dots, each one coated with a rather rare metal called *caesium*. This chemical is very sensitive to light. When a ray of light strikes a dot it knocks electrons out of it. Electrons are found in all atoms; they are extremely light in weight and each one carries a negative electrical charge.

In a motion picture camera, the chemical on the film changes light energy into chemical energy. In the retina of the eye there are chemical compounds that change light energy into chemical energy, producing a nerve impulse. In a television camera the chemical on the screen changes light energy into electrical energy. Each dot acts like a tiny photocell.

Since some part of the scene or of an object in the scene are brighter than other parts, light rays of different brightness are reflected to the screen at the same time. The brighter the ray of light that strikes a dot, the more electrons are knocked out of it. Keep in mind that there are thousands of dots on the screen.

The streams of electrons from the dots strike a plate called the target. The more electrons that strike a spot on the target, the more electrons are knocked out of that spot. Thus some spots on the target lose more electrons than other spots.

At this point, the target may be compared with the negative picture of a film camera. A film negative has light and dark spots. The target is made up of spots some of which have lost more electrons than other spots. A spot on the target that has lost many electrons is like the dark spot on the film negative. Both result from the brighter rays of light that have been reflected from the scene.

At the other end of the iconoscope tube is an electron gun. It shoots out a stream of electrons like a machine gun shoots out a stream of bullets. The electron stream from the gun is directed at the target. The target absorbs electrons like a sponge soaks up water. Spots on the target that lost more electrons absorb more of the electrons than do spots that lost fewer electrons.

The stream of electrons from the gun is called a beam. The beam moves across the target in a straight line, from left to right. At the end of each line the gun resets itself a trifle lower, and again sends a beam of electrons across the target in a straight line from left to right. This goes on until the gun has sent the beam across the target 525 times (405 times in Great Britain), each line just a trifle lower than the line before, from the top of the target to the bottom.

This movement of the electrons across the target is called scanning. It is like the movement of your eyes in reading this page. You start at the left side of the first line and read to the right across the page. Then you move your eyes back to the left side of the page and lower them just a little to the next line below. Again you read across the page to the right, to the end of the second line. Thus you scan the page with your eyes like the electron gun scans the target with electrons.

It takes just 1/30 of a second to scan the target from the

top to the bottom. This means that the image on the target changes 30 times in a second (25 times in a second in Great Britain).

The stream of electrons leaves the electron gun as a steady stream. When the beam bounces back, is reflected from the target, it varies from one instant to the next. This is so because the spots on the target have absorbed different amounts of electrons from the beam.

The beams of electrons that are reflected from the target are collected on a plate at the gun end of the iconoscope. These beams, which vary from one another, are called signals. The picture came into the television camera as light rays of different brightnesses. It leaves the television camera as electrical signals of different strengths.

While the picture was being changed from light rays to electrical signals, the voices and music were changed from sound waves to electrical signals. Since this book is about seeing and not about hearing we shall not tell you here how the latter is done.

The electrical signals from the television camera are amplified, strengthened, as they pass through several amplifying tubes or transistors in the amplifier. They are then carried through wires to the top of a high tower on which is the broadcasting antenna or aerial. The signals are ready to go off through the air. But they would not get far.

In the meantime, a machine called a transmitter has been producing powerful carrier waves. They too are carried by wires to the top of the broadcasting tower, to the antenna or aerial. These carrier waves are able to travel great distances through the air.

The electromagnetic waves that started as light in the television camera now unite with the carrier waves from the transmitter. As a result the carrier waves are altered. We say the waves are modulated. The modulated waves, the video (picture) signals, go off into the air. At the same time, other modulated waves, the audio (sound) signals, go off into the air from a neighboring antenna.

How are the modulated electromagnetic waves that are traveling through the air changed into a television program in the home? On the roof of the home is a high pole with crossed wires on it. This is the antenna that catches the signals which have been telecast. The signals are the modulated carrier waves. The antenna collects them and sends them down through wire to your television set. Sometimes the receiving antenna is placed right on top of the set. You receive the signals better if the antenna is high in the air.

In the television set, the signals first pass through tubes or transistors, where they are amplified. Then they pass through the tuner. Here you select the waves of the wave length that are carrying the program you want to see and hear.

The greatly amplified signals then pass to a tube that is narrow at one end and very wide at the opposite end. In the receiving set it is called the kinescope, or viewing tube. It includes an electron gun, like the one in the iconoscope.

When the signals reach the kinescope they start a stream of electrons flowing from the electron gun at the narrow end of the tube. A strong signal produces a strong flow of electrons; a weaker signal produces a weaker flow. The electrons are speeded up as they flow through the tube. They are directed in a straight line.

At the broad end of the kinescope there is a viewing screen. It is covered with a material that glows when electrons strike it. A spot on the screen glows brightly when a strong beam strikes it; it glows less brightly if a weak beam strikes it.

Now imagine these beams scanning the screen, line by line, 525 lines (405 lines in Great Britain) from the top of the screen to the bottom, all in 1/30 (1/25 in Great Britain) of a second. The scanning produces the pictures which you see on the television screen.

You see a picture because the images of all the spots on the viewing screen remain on the retina of the eye for the time that they are on the screen, 1/30 of a second. You see a moving picture because each entire image remains on the retina long enough to be overlapped by the succeeding image. It is like seeing moving pictures.

The sound-borne electromagnetic signals are changed into sound waves by other tubes in the receiver. Both light and sound signals are received at the same time. You therefore see the pictures move on the screen and hear the speech or music from the speaker together.

Now we can have television programs in color. Telecasting color programs is the same in principle as telecasting black and white programs, with some added complications.

As you know, white light from the sun or from an electric lamp is a mixture of different waves lengths of visible radiations, and can be separated into its component colors.

This principle is used in starting the color telecast. The rays of light that are reflected from the scene pass through the television camera lens. They are then divided into three beams by three color filters — a red, a green and a blue filter.

The color iconoscope has three screens. The rays of red light from the scene are focused on one screen. The rays of green and of blue light are similarly focused on different screens.

The color iconoscope has three electron guns. Each one scans one of the three screens. Three different signals leave the iconoscope to be carried through the air by carrier waves.

The kinescope in the color television receiver has three guns. The three signals — for red, for green, and for blue light — are caught by the antenna at the same time. They are amplified in the receiving set. The signals for red light then go to one gun, the signals for blue light to another, the signals for green light to the third.

The viewing screen of the color kinescope is covered with three kinds of spots, more than half a million of them. Some of them glow bright red when a strong beam of electrons strikes them from the electron gun which received the red signals. They glow less brightly when the beam is weaker. Similarly there are spots that glow green or blue, brightly or less brightly.

The spots are very close to one another, in clusters. As a result the colors blend so that you see a fairly good reproduction of the original color scene.

Why are red, green and blue used in color television?

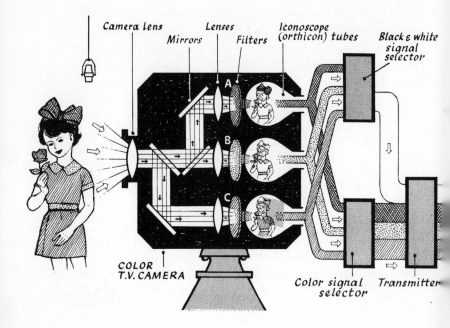

A color television broadcast

These are the primary colors. They may be mixed to produce most colors. The electromagnetic waves that carry the television program travel from the transmitter to the receiving sets.

They may travel directly from the transmitter to the receiver through the air, but this distance is limited by the

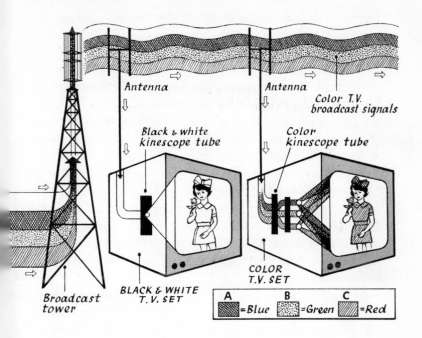

Antenna

Color T.V.
broadcast signals

Antenna

Black & white
kinescope tube

Color
kinescope tube

COLOR
T.V. SET

Broadcast
tower

BLACK & WHITE
T.V. SET

A	B	C
=Blue	=Green	=Red

nature of the waves. Television is broadcast by microwaves
that have very short lengths and very high frequencies.
Such waves travel in straight lines; they do not follow the
contour of the Earth's surface. Radio waves, on the other
hand, have long wave lengths and they are reflected from
the ionosphere layer that surrounds the Earth. They can

therefore follow the contour of the Earth's surface and travel great distances. Television waves can travel only to the horizon of the transmitting antenna.

In the early days of television broadcasting, the range of a transmitting station was an area with a radius of about 50 miles. Under these conditions few regions of the country enjoyed television programs, and these were not very spectacular because they reached rather small audiences.

Now a program originating in one part of the country may be seen in every other part of the country at the same time. Indeed, the means are already at hand for sending live television programs across the sea to Europe at the same time that they are broadcast here, and to receive broadcasts from Europe. The problem of sending the microwaves of television over great distances has been solved in a number of ways.

Many television programs do not come through "live," as they are performed. Such programs are prerecorded on videotape (video means to see). Both the picture and the sound are impressed on the tape. Many duplicate prints may be made and distributed. The tape may be "played back" to produce electromagnetic waves to broadcast simultaneously from many stations.

The range of live television broadcasts has been extended by the use of telephone lines to carry the programs, without impairing the normal telephone service. This has been made possible by the development of "superhighways" of communication. One such superhighway is the coaxial cable.

A coaxial cable is made up of coaxial units. Each unit is about the thickness of a pencil. On the inside of the unit is a copper wire about the thickness of the lead in the pencil. The wire is held in position by a series of disks made of a non-conducting material — a material that does not transmit or conduct electricity. Such a coaxial unit can carry without interference 600 telephone conversations in one direction at the same time, as well as a television program. The electromagnetic waves that carry the television program are changed into electrical impulses that are carried through the wire. At the other end these are converted into electromagnetic waves and are broadcast.

More television programs are carried over long distances by radio relays that also transmit a large part of the long distance telephone traffic. A relay station is made up of a microwave receiver, an amplifier and a microwave transmitter. Since the system uses microwaves, it works on a line-of-sight basis. Thus the receiving antenna must be in a straight line with and in sight of the sending antenna, since the microwaves travel in a straight line. Such an "invisible cable" of microwaves will carry without interference as many as 3,000 telephone conversations in one direction at the same time. A radio relay system has been developed that will pass along as many as 11,000 conversations at one time. Television programs are also carried by radio relays. Since these waves travel 186,000 miles in a second, the time that it takes to send a program a few hundred or even a few thousand miles is negligible.

In 1954 scientists and engineers at the Bell Telephone Laboratories conceived and planned a relay system that would have been regarded as fantastic science fiction not so many years ago. It was a daring and an imaginative idea — to put the relay stations far out in space beyond the

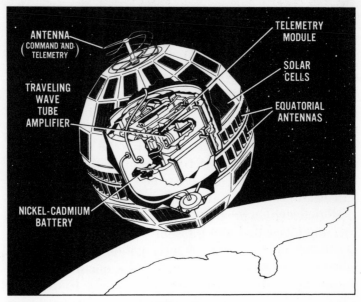

Telstar I

Earth, in orbiting satellites. On July 10, 1962, *Telstar I* was launched.

It was an "active" satellite, designed to receive, amplify, and transmit signals it received from Earth. Electromagnetic waves lose much of their energy in travelling through the air. Moreover, only an infinitesimal fraction of a wave will strike a target as small as a satellite far out in space. For commercial transmission, the faint signals *Telstar I* received from earth had to be greatly amplified — ten thousand million times.

The energy for *Telstar I*'s amplifier and transmitter came from solar batteries ringing the satellite and converting the

A dish-shaped antenna

A horn-shaped antenna

sun's energy for its use. There were antennas to receive
and transmit signals. The 15,000 parts of the satellite
were in a cylinder 34½ inches in diameter and weighing
170 pounds — a tiny speck in space.

Telstar I travelled 16,000 miles an hour in an orbit that
carried it from 3,002 miles from the Earth at its most distant point, to 593 miles at its nearest approach. It com-
pleted an orbit every 158 minutes. Scientists and engineers
were hopeful that such satellites would work effectively
for about 2 years. *Telstar I* actually worked for about 6
months.

To beam microwave messages to the satellite and to receive signals from it, an Earth station was built at Andover, Maine. The most prominent structure at this center is
the horn-shaped antenna. It is 94 feet high, weighing 350
tons, with an open end that measures 68 feet across. It is
housed in an inflated shelter which makes a dome 18 stories high. A huge dish-shaped antenna has also been used
to beam microwaves to the satellite and to receive such
waves in return.

The center at Andover has a powerful short wave receiver, an amplifier, and a transmitter, as well as equipment to
track the satellite in its orbit. All these are staffed by a
large corps of scientists and trained technicians. Similar
installations have been built in England and in France, so
that these countries may take part in the experimental program, and later in the plan for communication via satellite.

Telstar I passed over Andover 4 or 5 times a day. On
2 or 3 of those orbits it was also in range of European
stations. During these orbits, communication between

them was possible. When it passed over the horizon of either, communication was cut off. In the first day of its orbiting, a program was broadcast via *Telstar I* that was seen and heard throughout the United States and in Europe at the same time. Later, European stations broadcast programs that were clearly seen and heard throughout the United States.

Signals received at Andover are amplified, then relayed over networks throughout the country. The amplifier uses a maser, a device that magnifies the signal 500,000 times, without magnifying the radio noises received with the signal. The essential part of the maser is a ruby through which the microwaves pass, and in so doing are magnified in amplitude.

After several months, *Telstar I* was silenced by "radiation sickness." Remarkably, the scientists, from their distant position on Earth, were able to cure the trouble. However, it recurred, and *Telstar I* was silenced for good, unable to transmit signals.

On May 7, 1963 *Telstar II* was successfully orbited. It was hopefully designed to relay signals regardless of radiation. Moreover, its orbit carries it 575 miles at its nearest approach to Earth, to 6559 miles at its farthest, almost twice as far out as the orbit of *Telstar I*. This will make possible longer uninterrupted transmissions between the United States and Europe and the greater range will make it possible to transmit television programs to Japan and receive programs in return. *Telstar II*, however, has also had radiation trouble. It is estimated that 40 such satellites, following one another in orbit, will be needed for continuous communication. As one passes out of range, the next takes over.

But the scientists and engineers had in mind an even more imaginative and daring solution. If a satellite were placed in orbit 24,000 miles beyond the Earth, they reasoned, its period of revolution would be the same as the period of rotation of the Earth. Its orbit would take 24 hours — the same time that it would take a point on the Earth to make one rotation. If the satellite were in a position in relation to Andover, the two points would remain in the same relative positions, insuring continuous communication. At its distance, the satellite would include a far greater span in its range, almost a hemisphere.

Such a satellite, *Syncom*, has been launched on February 14, 1963. Unfortunately, contact with it was lost immediately. We may be sure that communications scientists will try again and again. They believe that such a satellite relay station is possible and practical. Communications engineers claim that satellite relays will be simpler and cheaper than extending the use of cables, and will reach distant lands more readily.

We started out to learn how we may see across space. It isn't difficult to understand, in principle. Light waves are changed into electromagnetic waves that travel directly through the air, or are carried to greater distances by coaxial cables or radio relays, or via satellite relay to the television receiver. Here the electromagnetic waves are changed back into light waves that produce the image on your television screen.

11

SEEING FARTHER INTO SPACE — TELESCOPE; RADAR ASTRONOMY

How far can we see? Farther than you may suspect. For example, the sun is approximately 92 million miles from the Earth. The nearest star in the sky is 27,000,000,000,000 (27 trillion or 27 million million) miles away. The fainter stars that are just barely visible on a moonless night are so much farther out in space that the distances can hardly be imagined, much less expressed in miles. We can see as far as the faintest star.

The sun is 860 thousand miles in diameter. This is more than 100 times greater than the diameter of the Earth. A million Earths would fit into the sun. All the stars are suns, most of them larger than our sun.

We may say, therefore, that we can see an object that is very far away if the object is very large and very bright.

We do not usually look at objects as large or as bright as suns. If we want to see farther we may do so by getting up higher. We can see farther from the top of a hill in the country or from the top of a high building in the city than we can from road or street level.

The surface of the Earth is round, not flat. Looking ahead, the farthest we can see is to the horizon, provided there is nothing in the way. The horizon is where the earth appears to meet the sky. The horizon appears farther away when seen from a height. We see farther around the curve, as it were.

In a forest the lookout tower is built on top of the highest hill. The forest ranger who is stationed there can then see farther to spot smoke that may mean a fire. On ships, the crow's nest is a lookout post near the top of the highest mast. The sailor who is stationed there on watch can see farther ahead of the ship than can the sailor who is stationed on deck at the prow.

But while we may see a far-off object, we may not see it clearly. Scientists have found the means to bring distant objects closer for a better look.

A long time ago astronomers, scientists who study the stars, built high towers to get closer to them, to see them better. But what difference would a few hundred feet make in seeing better an object many millions, even trillions of miles away? Astronomers still look at the stars from high places, hills and even mountains. They do so today to get above the smoke and dust of the cities.

The ancient astronomers could learn little, with the means they had, of the structure of the stars, or even of their vast numbers. However, they did record accurately the positions in space of many of the larger stars. And they learned how these stars change their positions with the seasons. From such knowledge, masters of ships were able to steer them to distant ports before the compass was invented.

It wasn't until about the year 1600 that science supplied help for the astronomers' eyes so that they were able to see more clearly the distant stars and planets.

You know that by that year spectacles were in common use to improve the eyesight of those who were eager to read the many books that were being published. Sooner or later, someone would try putting one pair of spectacles in front of another and looking through them. That is how the principle of the telescope was discovered.

"Telescope" means to "see far." The first telescopes were probably made in Holland, then the center of the spectacle industry, by some spectacle makers. The news of the new instruments got around quickly. Within a few years Galileo, an Italian astronomer, and Kepler, a German astronomer, had both made their own telescopes. These two names are very important ones in the science of astronomy.

It was Galileo who gave the name telescope to the instrument. His was a long tube with a long-focus convex lens at one end, and a concave lens at the other end, near the eye. With such a telescope the image is enlarged and seen upright.

With his first telescope Galileo was able to enlarge an object three times. Later he made one that enlarged the image of a star 33 times. With this telescope he was able to see and discover the mountains of the moon, spots on the sun, the moons of Jupiter, and many of the faint stars in the Milky Way.

At the same time Kepler made a telescope that used a convex lens as an eyepiece as well as at the other end of the tube. With such a telescope the image is enlarged but inverted, upside down. While it may be well suited to studying stars, such a telescope would not be as satisfactory in everyday life. It is difficult to get used to upside-down things in a normal world though it can be done. Remember the scientists mentioned in Chapter 3 who wore "upside-down spectacles"? Kepler's telescope can be improved by using another convex lens, called an inverting eyepiece, in front of the normal eyepiece. This results in an enlarged image right side up.

With the help of his telescope Kepler was able to formulate the three basic laws of astronomy that bear his name. First: the planets do not move in perfect circles around the sun. Their paths are flattened ellipses, with the sun off center (at one focus of the ellipse). Second: the speed of a planet is different in different parts of its elliptical path. Third: there is a constant relation between the distances of the planets from the sun and their times of revolution around it.

Thus the invention of the telescope in the first years of the 1600's enabled man to extend his sight farther out into space; to see farther and more clearly. Here was the beginning of the "space age."

Short telescopes were found useful in other ways. Ship's captains used them to sight distant objects, or to sight stars that helped them to navigate their ships. As "field" or "spy" glasses, telescopes were useful in military operations, to observe the accuracy of artillery fire, or to "spy out" the approaching enemy while he was still far off.

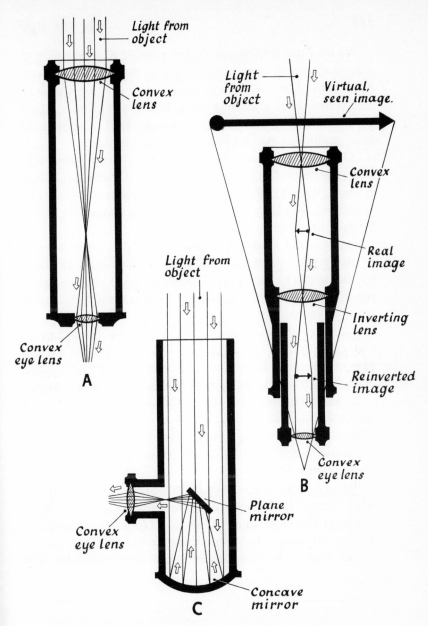

Telescopes: (A) Galileo's; (B) Kepler's; (C) Newton's

We may use field glasses to get a closer view of a play at a football game; or to study a bird in flight or on its nest. Such field glasses are made up of a pair of short Galilean telescopes. They may magnify 4, 6, 8 or more times. More powerful field glasses are made and are used by ships' captains, military men, field engineers, and others.

"Opera" glasses used in the theatre are also short Galilean telescopes. Because the distance in a theatre is relatively short, the magnification of these glasses is usually about two times. But they enable you to get a close view of the faces of the actors or the singers.

The tubes of field or of opera glasses may be shortened by using glass prisms in them. The rays of light are bent by the prisms as they pass through them, as you see in the drawings on page 87. Such field or opera glasses are called prism binoculars.

Concave mirrors converge light rays by reflection, as convex lenses do by refraction. The rays of light from a distant star reach the concave mirror as parallel rays. They are reflected and converged at the focus of the mirror.

Sir Isaac Newton, the great English mathematician and scientist, thought of using a concave mirror instead of a convex lens to focus the light rays. A telescope that uses a concave mirror is called a reflecting telescope. He made his telescope in 1668.

Because large mirrors are more readily shaped than are large lenses, the largest telescopes now are of the reflecting type. The largest one in the world today is the Hale reflecting telescope on Mount Palomar in California.

The Hale telescope has a mirror that measures 200

THE TWO HVNDRED INCH TELESCOPE

The Hale reflecting telescope. The 200-inch mirror
is at the base of the vertical cylinder seen in section

The Hale telescope. (Looking
down into the cylinder)

inches in diameter. It can gather approximately a million times as much light from a distant star as can the eye. We can now see 6,000,000,000,000,000,000,000 miles out into space (mathematicians would write this number 60×10^{20}) a distance far too great for most of us even to imagine.

Telescopes enable our eyes to explore the bodies far out in space. This is the universe of which we are a part. More and more of the universe has been brought closer and closer.

We have discovered that the many bright stars in the heavens are suns, most of them larger and brighter than our sun. These stars are very far distant from our Earth. The light that reaches our eyes from some of the faint stars will have traveled hundreds of years, at the rate of 186,-000 miles, approximately, a second, by the time we see it. The universe is very vast.

The universe is so vast that distances in it are measured in "light years." A light year is the distance that a beam of light, moving at a speed of 186,000 miles a second, will travel in a year. How many miles is this?

186,000 x	60	x 60	x 24	x 365
second	minute	hour	day	year

This totals approximately 6,000,000,000,000 (trillion, or million million) miles a year.

The nearest large star is four light years from the Earth. Many of the fainter stars are thousands of light years from the Earth. This means that the light from one of these stars, that enables us to see it, started its journey through space at tremendous speed long before there was any recorded history.

A spiral nebula was taken with
the 200-inch Hale telescope

On a clear, moonless night you can see in the heavens a pathway of light. This is the Milky Way. When you look at it through a telescope you see that this band of light is really made up of millions of stars. Such a huge cluster of stars is called a galaxy. Our sun and this earth are part of this galaxy.

With the larger telescopes we can see a number of galaxies. Each one is separate from the others. The universe is a vast space in which enormous galaxies move. With our large telescopes we see light from far off galaxies that has traveled millions of years before we see it.

Invisible electromagnetic waves are now used to extend man's sight into space. They enable him to "see" where the telescope cannot do so; to "see" details that are not visible to the eye through a telescope.

As early as 1924, a British scientist pioneered in the use of radio waves to measure distances in space. That is how we learned the height of the ionosphere. In 1946, scientists of the United States Army Signal Corps succeeded in bouncing a radar wave off the moon and detecting its return to Earth. Twelve years later, scientists at the Massachusetts Institute of Technology used a radar system 10,-000,000 times as strong to send a round trip signal to Venus. The following year scientists at Stanford University were able to get return signals from the sun. This is how radar astronomy began.

Radar astronomy sends out pulses of electromagnetic energy from powerful radio transmitters. These rays are directed against a solid body, or a cloud of gas in space. When they strike the body or cloud, the waves are scattered, absorbed, refracted, reflected, or changed in other ways.

Some of the reflected waves return to the sender. The time consumed between the sending of the signals and the return of the reflected waves enables the astronomer to compute the distance of the reflecting body. He can do so because he knows that the waves travel with the speed of light, which he knows. He multiplies the distance that the wave travels in a second by the number of seconds that it took the signal to make the round trip. From the differences in time from one signal to the next, the astronomer can describe, even picture the surface that he cannot see.

Thus radar waves may pass through the clouds that surround Venus and return with information about the planet's surface. Does it have continents, oceans, mountain ranges? Does the surface consist of a solid crust, sand, boulders, water? What are the physical and magnetic properties of the surface matter? Radar astronomy may answer these questions.

How much and how far we may "see" through radar astronomy depends on the development of transmitters that can convert greater amounts of energy with greater efficiency into radar signals. The energy output of the most powerful transmitter that we could produce would still be very little compared with the energy output of the sun, for example. Radar astronomy opens another window on the Universe.

Television, which enables us to see across distances on the Earth, now enables us to see far out into space. Special television cameras are built into rockets and satellites. They convert light energy into radio signals which they transmit to Earth, where they are converted into light signals — pictures of objects in space.

For example, Lunik III took a photograph of the side of the moon which we cannot see from the Earth, and transmitted it back to Earth by television on July 10th, 1959.

As this book is being written, we read of the invention of a new telescope that combines the principles of the optical (glass lens) telescope and television. Light rays from illuminated objects far out in space are transmitted by the lenses of the telescope to a television camera where the faint signals are amplified, then converted into pictures, still or moving, that can be directly screened or photographed. This telescope was designed primarily to track rockets, satellites, or space ships. It is so powerful that it can "see" an object the size of a billiard ball one hundred miles away.

Our eyes enable us to see what goes on about us. Science has produced aids that enable us to see so much more! We can see very tiny things with the help of optical and electron microscopes. We can see through things with the help of X-rays. We can see across space on the Earth with the help of television. We can see far out into space with the help of a telescope, of radar waves, or a telescope combined with television, or of television combined with radio waves. Sight is such a precious gift.

12

LASER LIGHT OF THE FUTURE

Just a few years ago (as this is being written) scientists found that they could change the nature of ordinary light so that it acquired unique and remarkable properties.

When ordinary white light passes through a ruby rod, atoms of chromium within it absorb all wave lengths of the light spectrum except those for red light. The atoms emit photons (particles of light) which fly about within the rod. Those striking the wall escape and are lost; those striking the highly polished mirrored ends are reflected. The reflected photons may collide with other chromium atoms that, thereupon, emit photons — a sort of chain reaction. The photons move with the speed of light (186,000 miles in a second), taking but an instant to travel the few inches of the length of the rod.

Such a rod is called a *laser* — from the initial letters of the words that explain its meaning: *l*ight *a*mplification by *s*timulated *e*mission of *r*adiation.

154

A laser light beam is quite unlike an ordinary beam of white light. It is made up of light waves of the same length. Ordinary light is a mixture of waves of different lengths. The waves of a laser beam travel in a straight line, in the same direction. Those of ordinary light radiate out in all directions. All the waves of a laser beam are "in phase," in step, crests matching crests, troughs matching troughs, thereby reinforcing one another. Waves of ordinary light often interfere with one another and cancel out one another. Thus, laser light is said to be "coherent," and ordinary light "incoherent." (Coherent light is never found in nature.)

Laser light waves, like those of ordinary light, may be reflected, refracted, and focused. Lasers, at this writing, are largely experimental, but scientists and engineers are finding extraordinary uses for laser light.

A small laser beam has been used to destroy growths on the surface of the body. Very small beams have been used to perform delicate operations on eyes, to attach corneas that have become detached. It is expected that beams will be produced that can be used to perform operations on single cells.

Large laser beams can produce heat intense enough to vaporize steel razor blades. Metals may be cut, drilled, or welded quickly and easily with them. It is expected that laser beams of the future will be able to produce temperatures like those on the sun's surface.

Communications engineers, studying the possibility of transmitting television programs and telephone conversations via laser beams, believe that a single beam will be able to transmit more than 1,000 television programs, or

1,000,000 telephone conversations at the same time. The wave length of laser light is much shorter than the smallest microwave now used in transmitting messages. Since laser light, like ordinary light, cannot pass through rain or fog, it will have to be "piped." That should not be difficult since the beam can be reflected or refracted around bends and curves.

A powerful laser beam, directed through a telescope to the dark side of a half moon, lit up a small area, and the light reflected from the moon was received through another telescope less than 3 seconds later, after a round trip of about a half-million miles.

Because the length of the waves of laser light is so much shorter than that of the smallest radio waves, the former can make 10,000 times as many measurements in space in a second as can radio waves.

A laser beam may be the "death ray" that science fiction writers imagined. A powerful laser beam travelling 186,000 miles a second may easily intercept and destroy by incineration a rocket or satellite travelling 15,000 miles an hour.

Scientists have now discovered metal lasers that promise still more wondrous achievements. They predict that a pinpoint of metal may convert an electric current directly into white light without loss of energy due to heating a filament (as in present light bulbs). Such a laser should last forever.

Thus, the never-ending research of scientists presents ever-expanding opportunities to learn more about natural forces, to control them, and to use them for the welfare of mankind.

INDEX

Absorption, of light, 77. *See* Light

Accommodation, of eye lens, 36, 48

Adaptation of the eye: to light, 38; to dark, 38

Aerial. See Antenna

Amebae, 21

Amplifier, 128

Angle: of incidence, 78; of reflection, 79; critical, 85

Antenna, 128, 129; of Telstar, 138

Astigmatism. *See* Eye defects

Astronomers, 54, 142-153

Astronomy, 142-153; radar, 151

Beam: light, 67, 82-85; electron, 127-128; laser, 154

Binocular: field glasses, 87, 146; microscope, 104

Blind spot. *See* Eye structure

Caesium, 126

Camera, 46; moving picture, 119-123; television, 124-135

Cartoon movies, 120

Cathode, 109

Cell, 105; light sensitive, 26, 27

Chloroplast, 13; chlorophyll, 13

Coaxial cable, 134-135

Color blindness. *See* Eye defects

Color pictures: film, 70; snapshots, 70; movies, 70; television, 130-133

Color sensation. *See* Seeing, color

Cornea. *See* Eye structure

Crossed eyes. *See* Eye defects

Earth, 142

Electron, 108, 126; gun, 109, 127; microscope, 105

Energy, light, 13, 14, 20

Enzymes, 13

Eyeball muscle. See Eye structure

Eye
  Types: fish, 29; insect
    (compound), 27; mollusc (octopus), 24; Nereis, 26; Planaria, 24;
    camera (human), 27;
    telescopic, 31
  Structure: cornea, 35-47;
    iris, 33-34; pupil, 34;
    muscles of eyeball, 43;
    retina, 26, 35, 36; blind
    spot, 42; fovea, 42, 43;
    cones, 36, 39, 41-43;
    rods, 36, 38-41; sclera,
    33
  Defects: astigmatism, 51;
    far sightedness, 47, 52;
    near sightedness, 47,
    52; crossed eyes, 44;
    color blindness, 71-72;
    night blindness, 40
Eye spot (Euglena), 32

Far sightedness. See Eye defects
Filter: color, 68, 69; in color
  television, 131
Fluoroscope, 115
Focal length. See Lens
Focusing: camera, 36; eye See
  Accommodation)
Food, role of light in making, 13
Food chain: role of light in, 16;
  role of diatoms and dinoflagellates in, 16; role of
  plankton in, 16, 18
Fovea. See Eye structure

Galaxy, 151
Galileo, 143
Gamma ray, 64

Headlight, 82

Iconoscope, 124, 131
Image: concave lens, 78, 100;
  concave mirror, 82; convex
  lens, 100; convex mirror, 81;
  plane mirror, 78; real, 78,
  100; virtual, 78; telescope,
  81; mosaic, 27; in brain, 46
Index: of reflection, 85; of refraction, 85
Infra-red radiation, 64, 72
Iodopsin, 36, 37, 40
Ionosphere, 133, 151
Iris. See Eye structure

Janssen (microscope), 93

Kepler, 143; laws of astronomy,
  144
Kinescope, 129; color, 131

Laser, 154-156
Leeuwenhoek, 92
Lens: bifocal, 50; concave, 48,
  88; condensing, 103; contact,
  48; convex, 48, 97: object,
  101, 102; ocular, 101; eye,
  defects, 35; 101-102; focal
  length, 97
Light, 11, 21, 63; as energy, 13,
  14, 20; coherent, 156; quality
  of, 76; absorption of, 77: reflection and refraction of, 75,
  ff; relation to plant life, 11 ff;

reaction of animals to, 21
Light ray, 77
Light year, 149
Lunik III, 153

Maser, 139
Microcosm, 91
Microscope, 91 ff; compound, 102; optical, 105; electron, 105; binocular, 104
Microwave, 133; receiver and transmitter, 135
Milky Way, 151
Mirage. *See* Optical illusion
Mirror: plane, 80; concave, 81; convex, 81; spherical, 80
Molecule, 105
Moving pictures, 119 ff; camera, 120; projector, 121; color, 70; stereoscopic, 123; slow motion, 122; time lapse, 123

Near sightedness. *See* Eye defects
Nerve impulse, 25, 37, 40
Night blindness. *See* Eye defects
Newton, 146

Ophthalmologist, 35
Optic nerve: Planaria, 24, 40; Nereis, 26; human, 41 *See* Eye structure
Optical illusion, 54 ff; 82, 123; mirage, 62
Optometrist, 48
Orthicon, image, 124

Periscope, 79, 87

Photochemical change, 36, 72-73, 113
Photons, 154
Photosynthesis, light in relation to, 13, 18
Phototropism, 15, 22, 24
Planaria, 24
Plankton, 16, 18
Plastic cable, transmission of light through, 89
Primary colors, 68; in television, 132
Principal focus, 81
Prism, glass, 65, 80; used as reflector, 87, 146
Projector: slide, 100; moving picture, 121
Protoplasm, 115
Pupil. *See* Eye structure

Radar: astronomy, 151; system, 151; waves, 64, 151
Radiation, 64
Radiant energy, 63 ff
Radioactivity, 64
Radio relay, 135
Radio waves. *See* Waves
Rainbow, 67
Reaction to light: Ameba, 21; earthworm, 23: Euglena, 23; paramecium, 21
Receptor, light, 21
Reflection, 75 ff
Refraction, 53, 75 ff, 97; of color, 69
Retina: blind spot, fovea, cones, rods. *See* Eye structure
Retinene, 37
Rhodopsin, 36-38, 40

Rod. *See* Eye structure

Scanning (television), 127
Sclera. *See* Eye structure
Searchlight, 82
Seeing, 33 ff; color, 71; by cats,
  40; hawks, 40; owls, 40; fish,
  29; insects, 28; jellyfish, 27
Seeing center, 40-41
Signals, electromagnetic, 129
Solar batteries, 138
Spectacles, 48, 93
Spectrum: color, 65, 66; electro-
  magnetic, 63; light, 64
Stars, 141, 149
Stereoscopic vision, 45; movies,
  123
Sun, 141
Syncom, 140

Target: in iconoscope tube, 126;
  in X-ray tube, 109
Telescope, 143; Galilean, 143;
  Kepler, 144; Newton, 146;
  Hale, 146; and television, 153
Telescopic eye. *See* Eye, types
Television, 124 ff; and space ex-
  ploration, 152; in astronomy,
  152; camera, 124

Telstar I, 136 ff
Telstar II, 139
Transmitter: in television, 128;
  in radar astronomy, 151
Transistor, 128, 129
Transparent surface, 77
Tuner, television, 129

Ultraviolet radiation, 64, 72
Universe, 149, 151
Uranium, 64

Vacuum tube: amplifying, 128,
  129; X-ray, 109
Valve. *See* Vacuum tube
Venus, 152
Viewing screen, television, 134
Vitamin A, 37-39

Waves: carrier, 120; electromagnetic, 128; microwaves,
  133; modulated, 129; radar,
  64, 151; radio, 63, 64; electromagnetic waves in astronomy, 151; light, 66, 78; frequency, length, 63

X-rays, 109 ff; in treatment of
  cancer, 116